MW00635262

SCRATCH YOUR BRAIN®
ALGEBRA

SERIES TITLES
SCRATCH YOUR BRAIN® A1
SCRATCH YOUR BRAIN® B1
SCRATCH YOUR BRAIN® C1
SCRATCH YOUR BRAIN® GEOMETRY
SCRATCH YOUR BRAIN® ALGEBRA

Written By
DOUG BRUMBAUGH
DAVID ROCK

Graphics By
ANNA ALLSHOUSE
BRAD GATES

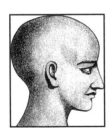

© 2008
THE CRITICAL THINKING CO.™
Phone: 800-458-4849 Fax: 831-393-3277
www.CriticalThinking.com
P.O. Box 1610 • Seaside • CA 93955-1610
ISBN 978-1-60144-146-1

Printed in the United States of America

Preface

We want to offer a special THANKS to Saretta Goss and Joe Walker for going through the entire manuscript. Their suggestions strengthened our work.

We hope you enjoy these problems. They are kid-tested. Many of them have been used in our middle and high school algebra classes, college-level mathematics methods courses, college-level mathematics courses, as examples in the textbooks we have written, and on our different web pages (http://www.colstate.edu/mathcontest and http://www.whitehouse.gov/kids). Over the years we have had many wonderful discussions with students, parents, teachers, friends, and each other as we published these problems. It has been a fantastic learning experience for us!

You will find that some of these problems are accompanied by a scoring rubric. These rubrics are a result of using the problems with students to encourage critical thinking and entice them to do mathematics. We realize that you might prefer different rubrics, but offer them as examples of how the evaluation of student work could be accomplished.

Some of the problem solutions give more than one way to arrive at the conclusion. Our experience has shown that it is advantageous to do one problem several different ways as opposed to giving students several problems that can be done essentially the same way. We offer these examples with more than one method of solution to encourage you to consider asking for different strategies to solve a problem. If you accept this challenge, you will find that you will stretch your own thinking in the process. And, if things run true to form, some students will suggest approaches that you do not think of.

About the Authors

Douglas K. Brumbaugh

Depending upon how you count, I have been teaching over 50 years. I tutored high school teammates, served as a lab assistant as a college undergraduate, tutored college friends, taught four years in the secondary schools in Adrian, Michigan, and then taught 35 years at the University of Central Florida. Several years of my UCF career found me teaching a class every day, all year long, in a local elementary, middle, or high school, where many of these problems were used. I received my B.S. from Adrian College and my Masters and Doctorate from the University of Georgia. I retired in 2004 but still do some presentations and writing.

David Rock

I am the Dean of the College of Education at Columbus State University. I received my B.S. in Mathematics from Vanderbilt University, M.A. in Mathematics Education from the University of Central Florida, and Ed. D. in Curriculum and Instruction from the University of Central Florida. I have had the good fortune of teaching mathematics in Florida, Mississippi, and Massachusetts at the middle and high school level, as well as at four universities. In addition to my time at Columbus State University, I have been a professor at the University of Mississippi and the University of Massachusetts, Dartmouth. I have conducted a multitude of workshops and seminars at local, state, and national conferences that incorporate many of the exercises posed in this book. My goal has always been to increase the interest in and enthusiasm of teaching and learning mathematics. Much of my inspiration comes from my wife Michelle (a former elementary teacher) and my wonderful children: Carly, Kyle, Katelyn, and Cassidy. By the way, Doug will never retire! Enjoy…….

Table of Contents

Exercise Number

NCTM Standard	1	2	3	4	5	6	7	8	9	10	11	12	13	14	15	16	17	18	19	20	21	22	23	24	25
Addition	■									■		■			■						■				■
Average																							■	■	
Division	■									■			■	■								■			■
Exponent																			■		■				
Factoring				■					■							■									■
Fraction																			■		■				■
Geometry							■		■	■			■	■	■				■			■			
Money																	■								
Mathematical Reasoning		■	■	■	■	■		■		■	■	■	■		■	■	■		■					■	■
Multiplication	■	■	■	■								■													■
Number Theory		■		■							■	■			■		■		■	■	■				
Order of Operations																									
Pattern		■		■								■			■					■					
Proof																									
Probability												■	■												
Problem Solving	■	■	■	■	■	■	■	■	■	■	■	■		■	■	■	■	■	■	■	■		■	■	■
Place Value																	■								
Rate																							■	■	
Substitution					■	■			■	■			■	■		■	■				■	■	■	■	■
Subtraction	■					■								■											
Use Formula		■						■	■		■		■		■	■		■	■	■	■	■	■	■	■

Exercise Number

NCTM Standard	26	27	28	29	30	31	32	33	34	35	36	37	38	39	40	41	42	43	44	45	46	47	48	49	50
Addition					■	■			■					■	■									■	■
Average																								■	
Division		■									■				■									■	■
Exponent				■	■				■				■			■	■	■		■	■	■	■	■	
Factoring														■					■			■			
Fraction							■				■										■				
Geometry			■	■																					
Money																									
Mathematical Reasoning			■	■		■			■	■	■	■	■		■		■	■	■		■		■	■	■
Multiplication		■			■					■			■	■	■				■						■
Number Theory	■				■	■	■	■						■	■	■	■			■	■	■	■		
Order of Operations																									
Pattern	■				■	■			■				■		■	■		■	■		■	■	■	■	■
Proof																	■	■	■	■					
Probability			■																			■			
Problem Solving	■	■	■		■	■	■	■	■	■			■			■	■			■	■	■	■	■	
Place Value								■				■													
Rate																									
Substitution		■		■													■	■				■			
Subtraction							■					■							■		■			■	
Use Formula		■	■											■	■					■	■	■		■	■

Exercise Number

NCTM Standard	51	52	53	54	55	56	57	58	59	60	61	62	63	64	65	66	67	68	69	70	71	72	73	74	75
Addition	■		■				■	■	■	■	■			■	■	■					■		■	■	
Average																									
Division				■			■	■	■	■	■	■	■	■											■
Exponent		■	■	■	■																	■	■		■
Factoring				■			■	■	■	■	■		■			■					■	■	■		■
Fraction					■		■	■	■	■	■								■	■				■	■
Geometry																									
Money																									
Mathematical Reasoning	■	■			■	■		■		■	■	■	■	■			■		■	■		■	■		■
Multiplication		■											■		■	■					■		■		■
Number Theory		■	■	■	■		■	■	■	■	■	■	■	■	■						■	■	■	■	■
Order of Operations																									
Pattern	■	■	■			■	■	■	■	■	■	■	■				■				■			■	
Proof				■											■	■			■				■	■	■
Probability																			■		■				
Problem Solving	■	■	■	■	■	■	■	■	■	■	■	■	■	■	■	■	■	■	■	■	■	■	■	■	■
Place Value							■	■	■	■	■	■				■							■		
Rate																									
Substitution				■	■		■	■	■	■	■	■		■	■				■			■		■	■
Subtraction		■													■	■									■
Use Formula	■			■	■												■	■		■	■				

Exercise Number

NCTM Standard	76	77	78	79	80	81	82	83	84	85	86	87	88	89	90	91	92	93	94	95	96	97	98	99	100
Addition		■	■					■						■	■			■					■		
Average														■	■							■			
Division				■	■			■				■		■	■	■	■		■	■			■		■
Exponent	■					■				■					■						■				
Factoring	■						■			■		■							■				■		
Fraction										■											■		■		
Geometry																									
Money										■										■					
Mathematical Reasoning	■		■	■	■	■	■	■	■	■	■	■	■				■		■		■		■	■	■
Multiplication	■			■		■	■	■	■							■	■	■			■		■		
Number Theory			■		■	■		■	■		■		■	■	■			■		■	■	■			■
Order of Operations																									
Pattern	■	■	■			■		■	■		■		■	■	■	■	■	■						■	■
Proof					■			■				■		■	■			■							
Probability						■																			
Problem Solving		■	■	■	■	■	■	■	■	■	■	■	■	■	■	■	■	■	■	■	■	■	■	■	■
Place Value	■															■		■	■	■		■			
Rate																									
Substitution		■	■	■			■		■			■			■	■			■		■		■		
Subtraction			■	■			■	■																	
Use Formula					■			■						■			■		■	■				■	■

Exercise Number

NCTM Standard	101	102	103	104	105	106	107	108	109	110	111	112	113	114	115	116	117	118	119	120
Addition	■		■					■		■	■		■		■					
Average																				
Division	■					■			■			■	■	■		■		■		
Exponent		■					■		■	■	■		■				■	■		
Factoring			■			■	■	■	■				■	■		■	■	■	■	■
Fraction														■					■	
Geometry																				
Money				■																
Mathematical Reasoning	■	■			■	■		■	■	■	■	■	■	■	■	■	■	■	■	■
Multiplication			■					■		■				■					■	
Number Theory	■	■		■	■	■	■	■	■	■	■	■	■	■	■	■	■	■	■	
Order of Operations		■																		
Pattern			■				■	■		■	■	■			■					
Proof	■					■												■		
Probability																				
Problem Solving	■	■	■	■	■	■	■	■	■	■	■	■	■	■	■	■	■	■	■	■
Place Value		■	■	■	■	■			■		■		■			■	■			
Rate																				
Substitution				■			■	■							■	■		■		
Subtraction																■		■		
Use Formula	■	■								■		■	■			■			■	

MEASUREMENTS

1. Boiling Point

The boiling point of water is 212 degrees Fahrenheit at sea level. However, the boiling point temperature decreases about 1 degree F for every 500 feet in altitude. At this rate, what is the boiling point of water in Albuquerque, New Mexico if Albuquerque's altitude is 5250 feet above sea level? Write an equation that can be used for any city's altitude using d for the boiling point in Fahrenheit and A as a given city's altitude.

2. High Voltage

A 60-watt light bulb is on for 95 hours before it burns out. What is the life of the light bulb in kilowatt hours?

3. **Who Weighs What?**

Three boys, Josh, Hans, and Simon, are sitting around on a farm with nothing to do. They walk into the barn and notice a scale used to weigh cattle. They decide to weigh themselves. Unfortunately, the scale begins at 100 kg. The problem is that none of them weigh more than 100 kg. They decide to weigh themselves in pairs. Josh was sure that he weighed the most.

Hans and Simon together = 132 kg
Simon and Josh together = 151 kg
Josh and Hans together = 137 kg

What did they each weigh?

4. **Not in That Year!**

April 22, 1988 is represented by 4/22/88. Notice that the product of the month and day is equal to the two-digit representation of the year. Considering only the dates from January 1, 1990 to January 1, 2000, inclusive, answer the following two questions.

1. In which years is it impossible for this unique trait to occur?

2. Write an explanation of why this trait cannot possibly occur in those years.

5. Twisting Time

How many minutes is it before 6:00 P.M. if 50 minutes ago it was four times as many minutes past 3:00 P.M.?

6. Cut the String

A piece of string is cut into two pieces at a randomly selected point. What is the probability that the longer piece is at least x times as long as the shorter piece?

7. Divide the Hexagon

You have a regular hexagon and a point located randomly somewhere inside the hexagon. Write an explanation of how you would draw a line through that randomly located point so that the line would divide the regular hexagon into two parts of equal area.

8. Locomotive

Two trains are on the same track heading straight for each other. One train is traveling at 90 miles per hour while the other is traveling at 120 miles per hour. If the trains are notified two minutes before they collide, they can avoid the accident. How far apart will the trains be two minutes before the impact?

9. The Track

A running track has straight parallel sides and semicircular ends. One lap of the track measures y long as you go along the inside edge of the inside lane. The innermost lane is Lane 1. The next lane out from Lane 1 is Lane 2. Lane 3 is the next lane out from Lane 2, and so on to the width of the track. Each lane is one meter wide. Assume that the finish line is at the center of one of the straight sides and perpendicular to that straight side of the track. The race we are discussing is a one-lap race that requires runners to stay in their respective lanes for the entire race so a staggered start is necessary to compensate for the radii of the circles in the ends. How far ahead of the starting mark for Lane 1 should the starting mark for Lane 2 be placed so both runners cover the same distance as they make their lap? Write an explanation of how you got your answer.

10. Circles in Box

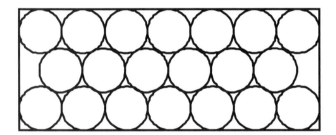

You have 20 congruent circles in a rectangle whose length (p) is greater than its width (q) and both are positive integers. All circles are tangent at points of contact with other circles or the sides of the rectangle, as shown. The ratio of length to width is $\dfrac{\sqrt{p} - q}{2}$. Find $p + q$.

11. License Plates

A state issues auto license plates with the following pattern: each plate has three letters followed by three digits (0 through 9). The letters can be in any combination. However, each digit must be equal to or greater than the one preceding it. (For example, 121 is not a legal number combination because the last 1 is less than the digit before it.) How many different license plates can the state issue? Note that all states eliminate some 3-letter combinations from consideration, but we will ignore that for this problem.

12. Martian License Plates

Believe it or not, the inhabitants of the planet Mars use the same alphabet as we do on Earth. On Mars, spaceship license plates consist of exactly three letters. Two license plates are considered identical if and only if they contain the same three letters in the same order. How many Martian license plates are possible if the letter Q must be followed directly by the letter U? Write an explanation of how you get your answer.

13. Pizza Crust

You make a 14-inch diameter pizza with a 1-inch wide edge. Your friend wants to make a 10-inch diameter pizza with the same percent of edge as your pizza. How wide will the edge on your friend's pizza be?

14. Complimenting Supplements

I am an angle that has a compliment that is 25% of my supplement. Who am I?

15. Moving Down

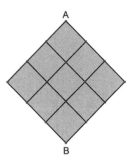

You begin at point A in the above figure. You are trying to get to point B. You can only move in a downward direction along the segments. How many different paths can you take that will get you from point A to point B?

16. Tyme Lee

Tyme Lee leaves home for work at exactly 8 A.M. daily. Averaging 40 miles per hour (mph), Tyme arrives at work exactly three minutes late. Averaging 60 mph, Tyme arrives at work exactly three minutes early. What rate will get Tyme to work exactly on time?

17. Lotta Coins

$1.65 is made up of pennies, nickels, and dimes. Half of the coins are nickels. List a set of coins that will solve this problem. Write an explanation of how you got your answer.

18. Looks Like Rain

A kid says that a 55 percent chance exists that he will go to the library tomorrow if it is raining at noon and a 30 percent chance if it is not raining at noon. The weather person on TV forecasts a 40 percent chance of rain at noon. On the basis of the information provided, what is the probability that the kid will go to the library?

19. Perfect Cubes

A cubic box contains 27 congruent large balls. Another cubic box the same size contains 64 congruent smaller balls. All 91 balls are made from the same material and have walls that are the same thickness. Each layer contains the same number of balls in each box, but the number of balls in a layer of one box is not necessarily equal to the number of balls in a layer of the other. In both boxes, the outside balls on each layer touch the inside wall of the box containing them. Which box is heavier? State a conclusion about m and n balls where both m and n are perfect cubes.

20. Thick as a Brick

A bricklayer is experimenting with patterns of bricks. The bricks are exactly 6 inches long and 3 inches wide. How many different unique patterns could be made with a row of ten bricks? A row must have a uniform height of 6 inches. There are only three possible patterns that can be made with 3 bricks as shown below. Our assumption is there is no mortar between these bricks.

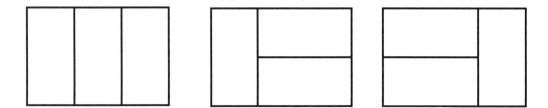

21. The Whole Distance

Suppose you walk for a total of 5 hours, first along a horizontal road, then up an incline to the top of a hill, and then back along the same route to where you started. Your pace is 4 mph on the horizontal sections of your walk, 3 mph as you go up the incline, and 6 mph as you go down the incline. How far would you walk as you travel the entire distance?

22. Shortest Altitude

Given a triangle with sides 15, 20, and 25 units, what is the length of the shortest altitude?

23. **Blocks Per Hour**

A kid rides a bicycle to school. From home, the ride is 5 blocks uphill, then 3 blocks level (flat), and finally downhill for 7 blocks to school. To avoid being tardy, the average speed must be 60 blocks per hour. Going uphill, the kid averages 45 blocks per hour. Going downhill, the kid averages 75 blocks per hour. To the nearest whole number, what must the average speed (in blocks per hour) be on the level part of the trip to make it to school on time? Write an explanation of how you got your answer (an equation will do).

24. **Back to School**

Suppose you travel directly between home and school at a rate of x miles per hour and return directly home from school at a rate of y miles per hour, x does not equal y. You take the same route both times. What is your average rate for the entire round trip? Count only the time you are traveling either from home to school or from school to home? The answer is NOT the arithmetic average $\frac{x+y}{2}$.

25. The Class

The six hundred members of the ninth-grade class are seated in rows, each of which contains the same number of chairs, and every chair is occupied. If five more chairs were in each row, everyone could be seated in four fewer rows. How many chairs are in each row?

26. Graphing

Tams, Gams, And Pams

There are 87 Tams. All 34 Gams and 49 Pams are Tams. If exactly nine Tams are Gams and Pams, then how many Tams are neither Pams nor Gams?

27. Ladders in the Alley

A 6-foot wide alley has both walls perpendicular to the ground. Two ladders, one 10 feet long and the other 12 feet long are propped up from the horizontal ground at the opposite corners to the opposite wall, forming an "X" shape. The feet of each ladder are firmly touching either the ground at the corner or the opposite wall. The two ladders are also touching each other at the intersection of the "X" shape. What is the shortest distance from the point of intersection to the ground?

28. Point

A point is randomly selected within the rectangle with vertices at (0,0), (2,0), (2,3), and (0,3). What is the probability that the x-coordinate of the point is less than the y-coordinate?

29. Cube Side

Given a cube with vertices P (7, 12, 10), Q (8, 8, 1), and R (11, 3, 9), what is the surface area of the cube?

PATTERNS

30. Three Digit Squares

A perfect square number is the product of a number and itself. For example, 169 is a three digit perfect square number since 13 x 13 = 169.

Find three 3-digit square numbers that together use each of the digits 1, 2, 3, 4, 5, 6, 7, 8 and 9 exactly once.

31. **Stuck in the Middle**

8, 6, 10, 13, 6, 9, 9, 3, 2, *N*, 7, 1, 1, 2, 7, 2, 4, 9, 1, 5, 3

Based on the above series of numbers, determine the value of *N*.

32. **2.52525...**

The number $2.\overline{52}$ can be written as a fraction. What is the sum of the numerator and denominator of that fraction after all common factors are divided out?

33. Take a Shot

What are the next two numbers in the sequence?
11, 31, 71, 91, 32, 92, 13, 73, 14, 34, 74, 35, 95, . . .

34. Rapid Growth

1, 5, 14, 30, 55, 91, 140, ___, ___, ___

Determine the next three numbers in the above pattern.

35. Random Cards

A girl and a boy are playing a game that consists of ten different numbered cards that are face down on a table. The faces of the cards are labeled using the numerals 1 – 10 (each card is numbered differently). If each person turns over a different card, what is the probability that the sum of the two cards is even?

36. Bike Race

You have entered a bicycle race on a closed circuit. After several hours of pedaling, you realize that the sum of one-fifth of the racers in front of you and five-sixth of the racers in back of you total the number of racers. If there are less than 50 bikers on the track, how many cyclists are in the race?

37. **Powers of 2 and 5**

A part of a cross-number puzzle looks like

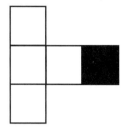

The puzzle calls for the vertical column to be filled with the digits from some 3-digit integer power of 5 and the horizontal row to be filled with the digits from some 3-digit integer power of 2. What is the digit in the shaded square?

38. **Units Powers of Three**

$\{3^0, 3^1, 3^2\ 3^3, \ldots, 3^{2000}\}$

How many numbers in the above set will have a units digit (ones digit) of one?

39. The Finest Pyramid

?
28
496
8128
33550336
8589869056
Find the number that begins this pyramid.

40. Picky Numbers

A number is called a "Picky Number" if it is a positive integer and the preceding and succeeding whole numbers are prime. In other words, 4 is a "Picky Number" since it is a positive whole number and both 3 and 5 are prime numbers. Find the average of all "Picky Numbers" less than 100.

41. Square Identity

Automorphic numbers are integers whose squares end in the given integer. Examples of automorphic numbers are $1^2 = 1$ and $6^2 = 36$. Find three additional automorphic numbers. Write a generalized statement about these numbers.

42. What Digits?

Given the sum of the squares of any three consecutive integers, what digits cannot appear in the ones place?

43. Powerful Operation

Imagine that a new mathematical operation has been implemented by the scientific community. The new operational symbol is &. Given that
1 & 1 = 0
2 & 5 = 7
3 & 4 = 17
4 & 6 = 2800
3 & 7 = 1844,

find the value of 7 & 5.

44. Threes and a Four

Find the sum of the digits of 33333333334 to the second power.

SCRATCH YOUR BRAIN® - ALGEBRA

45. What Is It?

If $a + b = 1$ and $a^2 + b^2 = 2$, then $a^3 + b^3 = ?$ Write to explain how you got your answer.

46. A Big Group

Suppose students arrive at school in groups. You are the first to arrive, and you are alone but still considered a group. The second group to arrive has two more people in it than were in your group. The third group has two more people than were in the second group. If there are 2,250 kids at your school on this day, how many groups will arrive at school, assuming they all meet the requirement of having two more members than the group before them? All groups except the last one must meet the "two more than the last group" requirement. Write to explain how you got your answer.

47.　**The Formula Is**

Given the sequence 0, 2, 6, 12, 20, 30, . . . , what is the formula that will give any desired term in the sequence?

48.　**A Billion Factors**

What two whole numbers that contain no zeros give a product of 1,000,000,000?

49. Difference of the Alternating Sequence

Given the sequence ⁻1, 2, ⁻3, 4, ⁻5, 6, ⁻7, . . . , what would be the difference of the mean (average) of the first 300 terms and the mean of the first 200 terms in the same sequence?

50. Greater Pair

H = {1, 3, 5, 7, . . . , 1,999}

Set H is defined as the positive odd integers less than 2,000. If ordered pairs (a, b) are selected from set H, how many possible ordered pairs will exist such that a < b?

51. Gauss Again

Find the difference between the sum of the first 1,000,000 even counting numbers and the sum of the first 1,000,000 odd counting numbers.

52. Funny Numbers

Find the next three entries in the sequence

0, 4, 18, 48, 100, 180, ___, ___, ___ .

53. An Operation

A new operation symbol has been created. Your task is to determine how the @ operation works. Based on each equation below, what would 7 @ 8 equal?

    1 @ 2 = 5

    3 @ 4 = 25

    4 @ 5 = 41

    5 @ 6 = 61

    7 @ 8 = ___

54. Composure

If $\triangle x = x + 3$ and $\boxed{x} = x^2 - 4$, find x such that $x^2 - \boxed{\triangle x} = 5$.

Write an explanation of how you got your answer.

55. Geometric Progression and Reciprocals

Find three integers that form a geometric progression so that the sum of the three integers

is 21 and the sum of their reciprocals is $\dfrac{7}{12}$.

56. Separation

Arrange the digits 1, 1, 2, 2, 3, and 3 to form a six-digit number such that the 1s have one digit between them, the 2s have two digits between them, and the 3s have three digits between them. What is the sum of all possible six-digit numbers formed under these conditions?

PROOFS

57. Divisibility by 3

You can tell if a number is divisible by 3 by adding the digits. If that sum is divisible by 3, the original number is divisible by 3. Although not usually necessary, this process can be repeated on the sum. For example, the sum of the digits in 135,476,892 is 45. Since 45 is divisible by 3, 135,476,892 is too. Repeating the rule with 45, the sum is 9, which is also divisible by 3, and thus, so is 135,476,892. Use your algebra skills and knowledge of place value to write an explanation of why this rule works.

58. Divisibility by 9

You can tell if a number is divisible by 9 by adding the digits. If that sum is divisible by 9, the original number is divisible by 9. This process can be repeated on the sum. For example, the sum of the digits in 135,476,892 is 45. Since 45 is divisible by 9, 9 also divides 135,476,892. Notice that the sum of the digits in 45 is 9, which is also divisible by 9. Use your algebra skills and knowledge of place value to write an explanation showing why this rule works.

59. Divisibility by 2

You can tell if a number is divisible by 2 by looking at the ones digit. If the ones digit is even, or, said another way, if the number ends in a 0, 2, 4, 6, or 8, then the number is divisible by 2. Use your algebra skills and knowledge of place value to write an explanation showing why this rule works.

60. Divisibility by 4

You can tell if a number is divisible by 4 by looking at the last two digits of the number. If they are divisible by 4, the entire number will be divisible by 4. Use your algebra skills and knowledge of place value to write an explanation showing why this rule works.

61. Divisibility by 8

You can tell if a number is divisible by 8 by looking at the number formed by the hundreds, tens, and ones digits. If the number formed by the hundreds, tens, and ones digit is divisible by 8, then the original number is divisible by 8. Use your algebra skills and knowledge of place value to write an explanation showing why this rule works.

62. Generalize Divisibility by Powers of 2

Work through the questions dealing with divisibility of 2, 4, and 8 in this book. Write an explanation that would generalize the procedure to 16 and beyond.

63. **Multiples of Four**

How many multiples of four from 1 through 1,000 do not contain any of the digits 6, 7, 8, 9, or 0?

64. **Mean Missing Number**

The mean of a set of five numbers is known to be 9.4, and four of the numbers are known to be 2, 7, 11, and 15. What is the missing number?

65. Age N Phone Number

Write your phone number, including the area code. Multiply that value by two. Add five. Multiply the sum by 50. Add your age to the product. Add 365 to the new sum. Subtract 615 from this sum. The result will be your phone number and age with your age being the ones and tens place digits of the result. Use variables to show how this problem works and write a paragraph explaining your solution.

66. Three Values

Roll three die. Select the top face value from one of the three. Multiply that value by two. Add five to the product. Multiply the sum by five. Add the top face value of one of the two remaining die. Multiply this new sum by 10. Add the top face value from the remaining die. Subtract 250 from this new sum. The result will be the three original die values. Use variables to show how this problem works and write a paragraph explaining your solution.

67. Many More Rectangles

How many retangles of any size are on an 8 x 8 checkerboard?

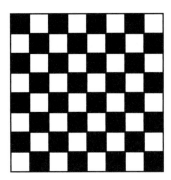

68. Pick Six, Including 3

Six distinct counting numbers are drawn from the set {1, 2, 3, ..., 9, 10}. What is the probability that, from those selected, 3 is the second smallest? Write to explain how you got your answer.

69. Pick One

I have one marble—either black or white—in a bag. I add one white marble to the bag, mix them up, and pull out a white marble. What is the probability that a white marble remains in the bag? Write to explain how you got your answer.

70. Pick a Composite

A box contains five ping-pong balls, each with a numeral on it. One ball has a one painted on it, one ball has a four on it, two of the balls are labeled with a seven, and one ball is marked with an eight. The balls are picked from the box one at a time without replacement and put in the order they are drawn, from left to right, to create a five-digit number. What is the probability that the five-digit number is a composite number?

71. Some Summation

What is the last digit of the computed form of the summation of J!, where J goes from zero through 1998? Write to explain how you got your answer.

72. 1 = 2

Let	$a = b$
Multiplying both sides of the equation by b gives	$ab = b^2$
Subtracting a^2 from both sides gives	$ab - a^2 = b^2 - a^2$
Factoring both sides gives	$a(b - a) = (b - a)(b + a)$
Dividing both sides by the common factor gives	$a = (b + a)$
Substituting a for b gives	$a = (a + a)$
Collecting like terms gives	$a = 2a$
Dividing both sides by a gives	$1 = 2$

Write an explanation describing the error in the above explanation.

73. **121**

The number 121 is a perfect square in the base 10 number systems because 11 x 11 = 121. Actually, 121 is a perfect square in any number base (greater than 2) in which it is written. Prove why this is true.

74. **Two Reciprocals**

Find the sum of the reciprocals of two real numbers, given that these numbers have a sum of 50 and a product of 25.

75. Speedy Arithmetic

Time yourself as you solve $\dfrac{1234567890}{(1234567891)^2 - (1234567890)(1234567892)}$.

Can you find a faster way to do the problem? Write an explanation of how you got your answer, emphasizing the quicker method.

PUZZLERS

76. Poetic Puzzler

A multiple of eleven I be,
Not odd but even, you see.
My digits are a pair
And when multiplied, beware,
Make a square and a
Cube out of me.
What number am I?

77. Hard Work Isn't Everything

Achieving one's goals is an important task in life. Some people say that hard work is everything. Others feel that knowledge is the key, while many feel that attitude is the key to success. If HARDWORK = 98% and KNOWLEDGE = 96%, explain why ATTITUDE = 100%.

78. Mystery Magic Square

M	21	94
3		

In a Magic Square, the sum of each of the three numbers in any row, diagonal, or column is the same value. Observe the above 3 x 3 magic square and determine the value of M. Write an explanation of how you got your answer.

79. **Reversal**

A kid was asked to subtract 3 from a given number and then divide the answer by 9. The kid subtracted 9 from a number and then divided by 3, getting an answer of 43. If the kid had worked the problem correctly, what is the answer?

80. **Phone Numbers**

A typical local telephone number in the United States can be dialed using 7 digits. Several areas of the country have started using 10-digit telephone numbers for local calls. If the entire country goes to 10-digit local phone numbers, exactly how many different 10-digit telephone numbers will be available such that the first digit cannot be a 0 or 1 and the fourth digit cannot be a 0?

81. Perfect Match

Suppose you randomly selected an integer from 1 to 1,000,000 inclusive and the number turned out to be a perfect square. What is the probability that the number is also a perfect cube?

82. The Hungry Caterpillar

A caterpillar will gain 2 grams of weight every day eating as much as possible. Not eating results in losing 3 grams of weight per day. If the caterpillar gained 5 grams over 20 days, how many days were spent not eating?

83. **Three Threes**

Use exactly three 3s and any numerical mathematical symbols to write two different mathematical expressions: one to equal 8 and one to equal 9.

84. **It Could be Reversible**

Determine all five-digit numbers that are reversed when multiplied by four.

85. Paying Taxes

In the country of Goldenania, the citizens pay numerically the same percent in income tax as they make in Goldenanian dollars per week. What is the maximum amount of money in Goldenian dollars that a person can take home after paying taxes each week?

86. I Scream for Ice Cream

At your favorite ice cream parlor, you decide to order a two-scoop cone. There are 14 different flavors of ice cream and three different types of cones. How many different types of two-scoop ice cream cones can you order?

87. **Old Math Books**

I have a very strange algebra teacher that collects old mathematics books. One day, I asked how many old math books were in the collection. Being a math teacher, the response was, "If I divide the books into two unequal whole numbers, then 64 times the difference between the two numbers equals the difference between the squares of the two numbers." How many old math books does my algebra teacher have?

88. **85 Four-Digit**

How many four-digit numbers contain the digit pattern 85 once and only once?

89. **20**

The mean of twenty unique counting numbers is twenty. What is the greatest possible value that can be used to yield this average?

90. **Average for Missing Link**

The average (mean) of five numbers is twelve. If the smallest of these five numbers is removed, the average of the remaining numbers is sixteen. What is the value of the number that was removed from the original five numbers?

91. **Dividing by Four**

If one is the remainder when a^2 is divided by 4, what would the remainder have to be if $(a + 5)^2$ was divided by 4?

92. **United States Senate**

Delegates of the 1787 Constitutional Convention established the framework for the United States Senate to include two senators from each state. Today, there are 100 senators. If a new five-member committee on mathematics education is to be created with no state represented by more than one senator, in how many ways can this new committee be formed?

93. Crazy Digits

A given two-digit number is seven times the sum of its digits. Reversing the digits gives a new number that is w times greater than the sum of its digits.

1. Will w be the same value for all two-digit numbers that are seven times the sum of its digits?

2. If your answer to part 1 is yes, what is the value of w?

94. UCF

In the product 9(YEAUCF) = 4(UCFYEA), find the six digit numbers YEAUCF and UCFYEA.

95. 72 Things

A bill for 72 widgets is $ $x67.9y$ where x and y represent digits. What is the cost of one widget? Explain how you got your answer.

96. Algebraic Poet

Add WHICH to WHAT and divide by four,
WHICH squared is now in store.
WHAT to WHICH is 35 to 1, you see,
The values of each, please tell me.

97. A Unique Number

Find the four-digit number *abcd* such that if you place a decimal point between *b* and *c*, the new number is the average of the two-digit numbers *ab* and *cd*. *a*, *b*, *c*, and *d* are all unique digits.

98. Dinner Check

A group of friends went to dinner and had a bill that totaled $288. When it came time to split the total cost of the bill equally, each person who was left (2 people left early) had to pay an extra $4.80 on top of their own part to cover the price of the two missing people. How many people were in the original dinner group?

99. Yippers

The following five-digit numbers are Yippers: 63,274, 63,850, 61,258, 65,218.

Some examples of numbers that are not Yippers are 83,927, 82,561, 75,361, and 68,134.

Which of the following numbers are Yippers: 29,038, 46,714, 25,674, 85,216, 67,452?

TRICKS

100. Two 8s

Using exactly two 8s and no other digits, write an expression equivalent to 100.

101. **Your Number**

Pick a number. Triple it. Add 12. Divide the new sum by three. Subtract four. What do you get? Use variables to show how this problem works and write an explanation of your solution.

102. **Talk About BIG**

What is the largest number you can write using three digits?

103. Three Times the Product

Find two different numbers between 0 and 100 such that each original number is three times the product of its digits.

104. How Much?

Two objects have a combined price of $6.80. One of the objects sells for $6.00 more than the other. What is the cost of the less expensive object? Write an explanation of how you got your answer.

105. **How Many Pages**

Suppose your job is to write the page numbers on a book manuscript. You start with page 1 (no Roman numerals) and you write 1,926 digits. How many pages are in the manuscript? Write to explain how you got your answer.

106. **163,163**

Write any 3-digit number. Repeat the selected number, writing the second beside the first, making a 6-digit number. Divide that 6-digit number by 7. Divide that answer by 11. Divide that answer by 13. The final answer will be the original 3-digit number. Write an explanation of how this works.

107. Alphabetical Polynomial

Find the product: $(x - a)(x - b)(x - c)(x - d) \ldots (x - z)$.

108. Forty-Eight

Sets of distinct positive counting number factors are created such that the product of each set of factors is 48. What is the least possible sum obtained from one of these sets of distinct counting number factors?

109. Did The Butler Do It?

One morning, a wealthy coin collector noticed that all but two of his very old and valuable Indian-head pennies were missing from their square display array. The owner asked his butler if he knew what had happened to the missing coins.

The butler explained that he awoke to the voices of three burglars in the middle of the night. The burglars were dividing the coins equally amongst themselves. They left the two remaining coins so that they each had the same number of coins.

After hearing the butler's explanation, the wealthy coin owner thought for a moment, then told the butler that he could use algebra to prove the butler was lying. The butler then confessed. Show how the coin owner knew the butler was not telling the truth.

110. Double or Nothing

Would you choose to make $10,000 a day every day for a month or a penny the first day, $0.02 the second day, $0.04 for the third day, and so, doubling the amount from the previous day for a month? Using the doubling method, how much would you make on the last day, and how much would you make for the month? Write an explanation of how you arrived at your answer.

111. How Can That Be?

How it is possible that 13 + 31 = 24 not 44? Explain.

112. **Four Four-Digit Primes**

a, b, c, and d represent different digits. *aaca*, *addd*, *bcdb*, and *bdac* represent four different four-digit prime numbers. Determine the sum of all four four-digit prime numbers (*aaca* + *addd* + *bcdb* + *bdac*).

113. **Fore!**

Pick any prime greater than three. Square it. Add 15. Divide by 12. What is the remainder? Write an explanation of why this works.

114. **Fift - E - Three**

If each of the letters represents a different digit 1 through 9, find the possible values for e in

the following equation: $\dfrac{f \cdot i \cdot f \cdot t \cdot e \cdot e \cdot n}{f \cdot i \cdot f \cdot t \cdot y \cdot t \cdot h \cdot r \cdot e \cdot e} = \dfrac{o \cdot n \cdot e}{t \cdot h \cdot r \cdot e \cdot e}$

115. **Which Is Greater**

If n represents any possible integer, which of these expressions $\frac{n}{2}$, $\frac{2}{n}$, $2n$, $n - 2$, or $2 - n$ yields the greatest value?

116. **Wacky Factors**

$$23 \times 96 = 2208 = 32 \times 69$$

Notice that the product of left side of the equation is equal to the product of the digits reversed on the right side. Find another pair of 2-digit numbers that share the same product when their digits are reversed. Double-digit factors (11, 22, 33, …) are not permitted. Prove why this is possible. (This problem was posed by Varavan Seingboon of Wattana Wittaya Academy in Bangkok, Thailand, and is used with permission.)

117. Fast Square

Pick a counting number. Square it. Take the next counting number. Square it. Find a fast way to find the second square. Is this process limited to counting numbers? Write an explanation of how you got your answer.

118. Subtracting Squares

Pick any counting number. Square it. Square the counting number that is one larger than your initial selection. Find the difference between the two squares. Subtract one from the difference and divide that answer by two. What do you get? Write an explanation why this will or will not always work, no matter what counting number you pick. Are you limited to counting numbers? Explain why or why not.

119. Special Fractions

If you add 3 to the numerator and the denominator of $\frac{1}{3}$, you get a new fraction that is twice the original one, or the original one is doubled.

Find a fraction that will triple when its denominator is added to both its numerator and its denominator.

Find a fraction that will quadruple when its denominator is added to both its numerator and its denominator.

BONUS Challenge—generalize this answer.

120. Some Formula

Give a statement that is true for all real numbers except 8, 23, and 1957.

ANSWERS

1.　ANSWER: 201.5 degrees F in Albuquerque. $d = 212 - \dfrac{A}{500}$

SOLUTION: $\dfrac{5250}{500}$ is 10.5. So, 212 – 10.5 = 201.5 degrees F in Albuquerque.

2.　ANSWER: 5.7 kilowatt hours

SOLUTION:

60 (watts) x 95 (hours) = $\dfrac{60}{1000}$ kilowatts x 95 (hours) = $\dfrac{5700}{1000}$ kilowatt hours = 5.7 kilowatt hours.

3.　ANSWER: Josh = 78 kg, Hans = 59 kg, and Simon = 73 kg

SOLUTION: Add them: (Hans + Simon) + (Simon + Josh) + (Josh + Hans) = 132 + 151 +137 = 420

Then 2(Hans + Simon + Josh) = 420

Or Hans + Simon + Josh = 210

Subtract the weight of each pair from 210 kg to get the weight of the third boy. Do this three times to get each boy's weight.

210 - 132 = 78 kg is what Josh weighs
210 - 151 = 59 kg is what Hans weighs
210 - 137 = 73 kg is what Simon weighs

4.　ANSWER: 1994 and 1997

SOLUTION: The only factors of 97 are 1 and 97, and 97 cannot be the day (must be less than 32) or month number (must be less than 13). Thus, 1997 is eliminated. The only factors of 94 are 1, 2, 47, and 94. Since no month has more than 31 days, none of those numbers work.

RUBRIC
4 possible points
1 point (content): Recognize 97 is prime
1 point (content): Correctly list the factors of 94
1 point (content): Recognize that numbers greater than 31 cannot be used
1 point (clarity): The explanation is clearly written.

5.　ANSWER: 26

SOLUTION: Let m be the number of minutes before 6:00. Then 50 minutes ago was 50 + m minutes before 6:00, which is the same as 180 – (50 + m) minutes after 3:00. Solving for m in the question $4m = 180 - (50 + m)$, gives $m = 26$.

6.　ANSWER: $\dfrac{2}{1+x}$

SOLUTION: Let AB represent the length of the string and P be the point on it such that AP:PB = 1:x. If AP has m inches, then the

length of PB is mx. The probability that the cut lies on AP is

$\dfrac{m}{m+mx}$ or $\dfrac{1}{1+x}$. Since the cut is equally likely to lie within the same distance from the other end of the string, the probability of either is $\dfrac{2}{1+x}$.

7.　SOLUTION: A regular hexagon has the center of the circumscribed (or inscribed) circle as a center of symmetry. Draw the line through the center of symmetry and the randomly selected point.

RUBRIC
3 possible points
1 point (content): Realize the center of symmetry exists.
1 point (content): Draw the line through the center of symmetry and random point.
1 point (clarity): The explanation is clearly written.

8.　ANSWER: 7 miles

SOLUTION: Work backwards beginning with the point of impact. We can find how far away from the point of impact each train will be from the collision point regardless of where the collision actually occurs. The 90 mile per hour train travels 90 miles per 60 minutes or $\dfrac{9}{6}$ or $\dfrac{3}{2}$ miles per minute or 3 miles in 2 minutes. The 120 mile per hour train travels 120 miles per 60 minutes or $\dfrac{12}{6}$ or 2 miles per minute or 4 miles in 2 minutes. Therefore, the first train will be 3 miles from the point of impact and the other train will be 4 miles from the point of impact 2 minutes prior to the collision. 3 + 4 = 7.

9.　ANSWER: 2π

SOLUTION: The two ends make a circle. Lane 1 would have a circumference of c_1 and Lane 2 would have a circumference of c_2. So, the difference between the two lanes is independent of the lengths of the straight sections, so $d = c_2 - c_1$. If r is the radius of the circle with circumference c_1 in meters, then $r + 1$ is the radius of the circle with circumference c_2.

$c_1 = 2\pi r$
$c_2 = 2\pi(r + 1)$
$d = c_2 - c_1$
$\quad = 2\pi(r + 1) - 2\pi r$
$\quad = 2\pi r + 2\pi - 2\pi r$
$\quad = 2\pi$

RUBRIC
4 possible points
1 point (content): Realize that the two ends make a circle.
1 point (content): Realize that the straights do not impact the conclusions.
1 point (content): Formulas and computations are used correctly.
1 point (clarity): The explanation is clearly written.

10.   ANSWER: $p + q$ = 154

SOLUTION: Let r = the radius of each circle.
Then $14r = p$
Consider the centers of any three mutually tangent circles and the
equilateral triangle they form. The height of that triangle is $r\sqrt{3}$,
and the width of the rectangle, $q = 2r + 2r\sqrt{3}$

$$\frac{p}{q} = \frac{14r}{2r(1+\sqrt{3})}$$
$$= \frac{7}{(1+\sqrt{3})}$$
$$= \left(\frac{7}{(1+\sqrt{3})}\right)\left(\frac{(1-\sqrt{3})}{(1-\sqrt{3})}\right)$$
$$= \frac{7(1-\sqrt{3})}{^-2}$$
$$= \frac{7(\sqrt{3}-1)}{2}$$
$$= \frac{\sqrt{(7^2)(3)}-7}{2}$$
$$= \frac{\sqrt{147}-7}{2}$$

So, $p = 147$ and $q = 7$, making $p + q = 154$.

11.   ANSWER: 3,866,720

SOLUTION: Look at the number combinations. Start with 999
and work backward, listing the possible number of combinations.
You will generate the sequence of triangular numbers: 1, 3,
6, 10, 15, 21, 28, 36, 45, 55. Adding these, you get 220 legal
number combinations. The letter combinations total (26)(26)(26)
= 17,576. So all total, there are (17,576)(220) = 3,866,720 legal
license plates.

12.   ANSWER: 15,675

SOLUTION: If the letter Q were not in the alphabet, the number
of possible license plates would be 25 X 25 X 25=15,625. We
must add to this amount the number of plates that include the
letter Q. If Q is the first letter, then the second letter is U and any
letter other than Q can be the third. We cannot have a Q in the
third slot because it must be followed by a U and there is no
fourth slot. Thus, we have just added 25 more plates.
 If Q is the second letter, then the third letter must be U and the
first letter can be any letter other than Q, again because it must
be followed by U. This arrangement gives 25 more possible
plates, for a grand total of 15,675.

RUBRIC
5 possible points
1 point (content): Realize the are 15,625 plates with no Q.
1 point (content): Realize there cannot be a Q in the third or last
                           slot.
1 point (content): Realize that if Q is in the first slot, there are 25
                           additional possible plates.
1 point (content): Realize that if Q is in the second slot, there are
                           25 possible plates.

1 point (clarity): The additional explanation is clearly written.

13.   ANSWER: 0.71 inches

SOLUTION: The 14-inch pizza has a radius of 7 inches yielding
an area of 49π square inches. Without the edge, the radius is
6 inches yielding an area of 36π square inches. So the area of
the edge is 13π square inches. The percent of crust is $\frac{13\pi}{49\pi}$ =
0.265. Your friend needs to make the edge 0.265% of the pizza.

Then $\frac{13\pi}{49\pi} = \frac{x}{25\pi}$, then $x = 6.63\pi$ square inches. The area
of the 10-inch pizza is 25π square inches. Therefore, the area of
the pizza without the edge is 18.37π square inches. The radius of
the pizza that does not have the edge is the square root of 18.37
or 4.29 inches. The radius of the 10-inch pizza with the edge is
5 inches. 5 inches – 4.29 inches = 0.71 inches. Therefore 0.71
inches is the width of the edge.

14.   ANSWER: 60

SOLUTION: Let x be the angle.
$90 - x$ would be the compliment.
$180 - x$ would be the supplement.
Since the compliment is 25% of the supplement,

$90 - x = 0.25(180 - x)$, giving $90 - x = \frac{180 - x}{4}$. Solving 360
$- 4x = 180 - x$ for x, $3x = 180$ and $x = 60$.

15.   ANSWER: 20

SOLUTION: Think of Pascal's Triangle.

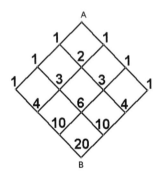

The numbers represent the number of paths you can take to get
to each point.

Notice the pattern that each value is the sum of the values above
or to the right and left.

16.   ANSWER: 48 mph

SOLUTION: Let t be the time required for Tyme to get to work on
time.
Three minutes = 0.05 hours
Since distance = rate x time, we can say (40mph)(t + 0.05).
Also, distance = (60 mph)(t – 0.05)
Since distance traveled is the same for both rates,
      $40(t + 0.05) = 60(t – 0.05)$.

$$t + 0.05 = \left(\frac{3}{2}\right)(t - 0.05)$$
$$2t + 0.1 = 3t - 0.15$$
$$t = 0.25 \text{ hours}$$

So, distance = 40(0.25 + 0.05) = (40)(0.03) = 12 miles.
That means 12 = r(0.25)
$$r = 48 \text{ mph}$$
OR
$$40(t + 0.05) = 60(t - 0.05)$$
$$40t + 2 = 60t - 3$$
$$5 = 20t$$
$$0.25 = t$$
The distance from home to work is 40(0.25 + 0.05), or 12 miles.

The average speed will be $\dfrac{12}{0.25}$ = 48 mph.

17.   ANSWER: (p, d, n) = (0, 11, 11), (5, 9, 14), (10, 7, 17), (15, 5, 20), (20, 3, 23), (25, 1, 26) (NOTE the order change to penny, dime, and nickel.)

SOLUTION: Let p = pennies, n = nickels, and d = dimes.
1.65 = 0.01p + 0.05n + 0.10d

Since we have a value ending in 5, we know the pennies must appear in multiples of 5.

If we have an odd number of pennies, we must have an even number of nickels or we will not get an odd sum in the end.

Since half the coins are nickels, the total number of pennies and dimes must equal the number of nickels. This becomes a guess and check process after the number of pennies is selected.

(0, 11, 11)
(5, 9, 14)
(10, 7, 17)
(15, 5, 20)
(20, 3, 23)
(25, 1, 26)

RUBRIC
4 possible points
1 point (content): Realize pennies must be in multiples of five.
1 point (content): Realize an odd number of pennies means an even number of nickels.
1 point (content): Realize the number of pennies + dimes = the number of nickels.
1 point (clarity): The explanation is clearly written.

18.   ANSWER: 40%

SOLUTION: P(The kid goes to the library and it rains) = 0.55 x 0.40 = 0.22.
P(The kid goes to the library and it does not rain) = 0.30 x 0.60 = 0.18.
The probability that the kid will go to the library is the probability that the kid goes to the library and it rains or the probability that the kid goes to the library and it does not rain. Since it cannot both rain and not rain at noon, we add the probabilities. 0.22 + 0.18 = 0.40.

19.   ANSWER: Neither—they weigh the same.

SOLUTION: The volume of the large ball is $\dfrac{64}{27}$ that of the smaller ball. There are $\dfrac{27}{64}$ as many large balls as there are small balls. Thus, the two boxes must weigh the same. This is true for any pair of cubes.

RUBRIC
3 possible points
1 point (content): Realize the reciprocals exist.
1 point (content): Realize the boxes weigh the same.
1 point (clarity): The explanation is clearly written.

20.   ANSWER: 89

SOLUTION: This follows a Fibonacci sequence beginning with 1 brick (being the second Fibonacci number) which is one way and two bricks which is 2 ways (third Fibonacci number). 1, 1, 2, 3, 5, 8, 13, 21, 34, 55, 89

21.   ANSWER: 20 miles

SOLUTION: Let x = the horizontal distance and y = the incline distance.

Time = distance divided by rate. The total time of travel is
$$5 = \frac{x}{4} + \frac{y}{3} + \frac{y}{6} + \frac{x}{4}$$
$$= \frac{2x}{4} + \frac{3y}{6}$$
$$= \frac{x}{2} + \frac{y}{2}$$
and 10 = x + y, which is half the distance. The total distance is 2(x + y) = 2(10), or 20.

22.   ANSWER: 12 units

SOLUTION: Divide each side by 5 and you have a 3, 4, 5 right triangle. Thus, the 15 and 20 unit sides are perpendicular to each other and also are altitudes.

The area of the triangle is $\dfrac{(15)(20)}{2}$, or 150 square units.
The third altitude is perpendicular to the hypotenuse of the triangle.

With the hypotenuse as the base of the triangle,
$$\frac{(25)(altitude)}{2} = 150 \text{ square units}.$$

So, altitude = $\dfrac{(150)(2)}{25}$, which is 12 units, and this is the shortest one.

23.   ANSWER: 66 bph

SOLUTION: Since distance = rate x time, a total distance of 15

blocks at 60 blocks per hour would take $\dfrac{15}{60} = \dfrac{1}{4}$ hours , or

0.25 hours. Going 5 blocks uphill at a rate of 45 blocks per hour

means it would take $\dfrac{5}{45} = \dfrac{1}{9}$ hours to get uphill. Going 7

blocks downhill at a rate of 75 blocks per hour means it would

take $\dfrac{7}{75}$ hours to get down the hill. Let t be the amount of time
the kid bicycles the 3 flat blocks. Then,

$$\dfrac{1}{9} \text{ hours } + \dfrac{7}{75} \text{ hours } + t = \dfrac{1}{4} \text{ hours }.$$

$$\text{Solving, } t = \dfrac{123}{2700} \text{ hours}.$$

Using: $\text{distance}_{flat} = \text{rate}_{flat} \times \text{time}_{flat}.$

$$3 \text{ blocks} = r \times \dfrac{123}{2700} \text{ hours}$$

$$= 66.85, \text{ or } 60 \text{ blocks per hour to}$$
$$\text{get to school on time.}$$

OR

$$\dfrac{15}{\dfrac{5}{45}+\dfrac{3}{x}+\dfrac{7}{75}} = 60 \qquad \text{Solve for x and you get 65.85,}$$

or 66 blocks per hour to get to school on time.

RUBRIC
3 possible points
1 point (content): Realize the need to add the partial rates.
1 point (content): Realize the need to set the sum equal to 60.
1 point (clarity): The explanation is clearly written.

24.   ANSWER: $\dfrac{2xy}{x+y}$

SOLUTION: By definition, average rate = $\dfrac{\text{total distance}}{\text{total time}}$.

If the distance from home to school was d, the rate was $\dfrac{d}{x}$.

Similarly, the rate from school to home was $\dfrac{d}{y}$. The average

rate is $\dfrac{d+d}{\dfrac{d}{x}+\dfrac{d}{y}} = \dfrac{2d}{\dfrac{dy+dx}{xy}} = \dfrac{2dxy}{d(y+x)} = \dfrac{2xy}{y+x}$. Initially this
might appear incorrect, but remember that one rate is greater
than the other. At the greater rate, the travel takes less time.
Thus, the arithmetic average of the two rates will not work here.

25.   ANSWER: 25

SOLUTION: Let r = the number of rows and c = the number of
chairs in each row. Since each row contains the same number

of chairs, $rc = 600$ and $c = \dfrac{600}{r}$. (Five more chairs in each row
and four fewer rows means)

$$600 = (r-4)(c+5),$$

$$= rc - 4c + 5r - 20.$$

Since $c = \dfrac{600}{r}$, $600 = (r)\left(\dfrac{600}{r}\right) - (4)\left(\dfrac{600}{r}\right) + 5r - 20$

$$= 600 - \dfrac{2400}{r} + 5r - 20.$$

Simplifying gives $0 = 5r - \dfrac{2400}{r} + 20.$

Multiplying both sides by r, $0 = 5r^2 + 20r - 2400$

$$= r^2 + 4r - 480.$$

Factoring, $0 = (r+20)(r-24)$, and $r = ^-20$ or 24. Since the
number of rows is positive, $^-20$ cannot be a solution. So, $r = 24$

and $c = 25$ chairs in each row.

26.   ANSWER: 13

SOLUTION:

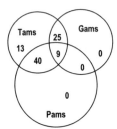

From the diagram, the number of Tams that are neither Pams nor
Gams is given as $87 - (25 + 9 + 40) = 87 - 74 = 13.$

27.   ANSWER: ≈ 4.52 feet

SOLUTION: Consider the two ladders as two line segments on a
grid.
The 10-foot ladder is the hypotenuse of a 6-8-10 right triangle.
Let the shorter ladder extend from (0,0) to (6,8).
The 12-foot ladder is the hypotenuse of a right triangle with a
base of 6, and using the Pythagorean theorem gives the height of

the other leg to be $\sqrt{108}$.

Let the longer ladder extend from (6,0) to (0, $\sqrt{108}$).
Solve for the slope and y–intercept to find the equations of the two
lines.

The shorter ladder equation $y = \frac{4}{3} x$ or $x = \frac{3}{4} y$. (1)

The longer ladder has the equation $y = \frac{-\sqrt{108}}{6} x + \sqrt{108}$. (2)
Substitute (1) in (2) and solve for y.

The answer is $\dfrac{\sqrt{108}}{1 + \dfrac{\sqrt{108}}{8}} \approx 4.5203$ feet.

28.   ANSWER: 0.667

SOLUTION: The line $y = x$ represents all the points for which the x- and y-coordinates are equal. Points above the line represent points for which the x- coordinate is less than the y-coordinate, and points below the line represent points for which the x-coordinate is greater than the y-coordinate. If you shade the region of the rectangle above the line $y = x$, this represents the region of the rectangle where all points have the x-coordinate less than the y-coordinate. The total area of this rectangle is 2(3) or 6 square units. The line $y = x$ crosses the right side of the rectangle at point (2,2). The region below the line is a triangle with height 2 and base 2, and has an area of (0.5)(2)(2) = 2 square units. The ratio of the area above the line to the whole rectangle is $\frac{4}{6}$ or 0.667. The probability that a randomly chosen point has the x-coordinate less than the y-coordinate is 0.667.

29.

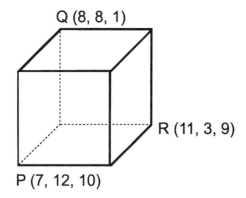

Q (8, 8, 1)

R (11, 3, 9)

P (7, 12, 10)

ANSWER: 294 square units

SOLUTION: PQR is an equilateral triangle since all three sides are diagonals of congruent squares.
PQ = QR = PR. Looking at P and R, the dimensional differences are 4, ⁻9, and ⁻1. Using 4 and ⁻9 gives a hypotenuse of

$$\sqrt{4^2 + (^-9)^2} = \sqrt{16 + 81} = \sqrt{97}$$, and then

inserting the ⁻1 gives

$$PQ = \sqrt{97 + (^-1)^2} = \sqrt{98}$$, which is

$$\sqrt{(49)(2)} = 7\sqrt{2}$$ units.

But that makes the side length of the cube be 7 units.
Thus, the surface area of the cube is
$6(7^2) = 6(49) = 294$ square units.

30.   ANSWER: 361, 529, 784

SOLUTION: The 3-digit squares are: 169, 196, 256, 289, 324, 361, 529, 576, 625, 729, 784, 841, and 961.

31.   ANSWER: 8

SOLUTION: The first number (8) is the sum of the last two numbers (5 + 3). The second number 6 is the sum of the second to last two numbers (1 + 5), and so on until N would be the sum of 7 + 1.

32.   ANSWER: 349

SOLUTION: Let $N = 2.\overline{52}$.

Then $100N = 252.\overline{52}$.

Subtracting the first equation from the second gives

$99N = 250$ and $N = \dfrac{250}{99}$.

Since 99 and 250 are relatively prime, the sum must be 349.

33.   ANSWER: 16 and 76

SOLUTION: The numbers are two-digit prime number reversed. 59 is the last prime number in the given sequence, so 61 and 67 would be the next primes.

34.   ANSWER: 204, 285, 385

SOLUTION: Begin with the first perfect square. To find the second term, add the second perfect square to the previous term 1 + 4. To find the third term, add the third perfect square to the previous term, 5 + 9. To find the eighth term, add the 8th perfect square (64) to the previous term 140 + 64 = 204. To find the ninth term, add the 9th perfect square (81) to the previous term 204 + 81 = 285. To find the tenth term, add the 10th perfect square (100) to the previous term 285 + 100 = 385.

35.   ANSWER: $\dfrac{4}{9}$ or approximately 0.44

SOLUTION: To get an even sum, the two cards must both be even or both odd. Therefore, the first numbered card can be selected ten ways but the second numbered card can only be selected in four ways (in order to have the same parity – both even or both odd). Thus, the probability is

$$\dfrac{(10)(4)}{(10)(9)} \text{ or } \dfrac{40}{90} \text{, or } \dfrac{4}{9} .$$

36.   ANSWER: 31 cyclists

SOLUTION: Since you are on a closed circuit track, the racers in front of you are also in back of you. The two fractions given have a LCD of 30, so you must see 30 other cyclists (in front or back of you). Including yourself in the race, there are 31 cyclists.

$$\dfrac{1}{5} + \dfrac{5}{6} = \dfrac{31}{30} . \quad \dfrac{1}{5} \text{ of 30 is 6 and } \dfrac{5}{6} \text{ of 30 is 25 and 6 + 25 = 31.}$$

37.   ANSWER: 6

SOLUTION: The 3-digit powers of 5 are 125 and 625. Thus, the ones digit of the 3-digit power of 2 must be a 2. That makes the desired power of 2 be 256, making the digit in the shaded square a 6.

38.   ANSWER: 501

SOLUTION: Look for a pattern.

$3^0 = 1$	$3^4 = 81$
$3^1 = 3$	$3^5 = 243$
$3^2 = 9$	$3^6 = 729$
$3^3 = 27$	$3^7 = 2{,}187$

Notice the pattern of the units digit of 1, 3, 9, 7. There are four possible units digits. The set contains 2001 elements. Dividing 2000 by 4 gives 500 with a remainder 1. If you ignore 3^0, there are 2000 elements where a units digit of 1 will occur at least 500 times. The catch is there are 2001 numbers where the first and last will have a units digit of one. Therefore, there will be 501 numbers with a units digit of one in this set.

39.   ANSWER 6

SOLUTION: Perfect numbers (In perfect numbers, the sum of the factors, excluding the number itself, equals the number. The factors of 6 are 1, 2, 3, and 6. Exclude 6 and you have the sum 1 + 2 + 3 = 6.)

40.   ANSWER: 30.5

SOLUTION: There are 8 picky numbers less than 100: 4, 6, 12, 18, 30, 42, 60, and 72. The sum of the number is 244. The mean is $\frac{244}{8} = 30.5$.

41.   ANSWER: Answers will vary. Some samples: 5, 25, and 625.

SOLUTION: $5^2 = 25$; $25^2 = 625$; $625^2 = 390625$. In general, any integer ending in 1, 5, or 6 is automorphic.

RUBRIC
4 possible points
1 point (content): Realize any integer ending in 1 is automorphic
1 point (content): Realize any integer ending in 5 is automorphic
1 point (content): Realize any integer ending in 6 is automorphic
1 point (clarity): The explanation is clearly written.

42.   ANSWER: 1, 3, 6, and 8

SOLUTION: Let the integers be $(x - 1)$, x, and $(x + 1)$.
The sum of the squares would be $(x - 1)^2 + x^2 + (x + 1)^2 = 3x^2 + 2$.
Try some numbers and see the sum always ends in 0, 2, 4, 5, 7, or 9.

43.   ANSWER: ‑61,318

SOLUTION: $a \,\&\, b = a^b - b^a$ for all examples given
$1^1 - 1^1 = 1 - 1 = 0$
$2^5 - 5^2 = 32 - 25 = 7$
$3^4 - 4^3 = 81 - 64 = 17$
$4^6 - 6^4 = 4096 - 1296 = 2800$
$3^7 - 7^3 = 2187 - 343 = 1844$
$7^5 - 5^7 = 16807 - 78125 = ‑61318$

44.   ANSWER: 67

SOLUTION: Observe the following pattern:
$34^2 = 1156$
$334^2 = 111556$
$3334^2 = 11115556$
$33334^2 = 1111155556$

Continuing this pattern idea,
$33333333334^2 = 1111111111155555555556$

The sum of the digits would be
  $11(1) + (10)5 + 6 = 11 + 50 + 6 = 67$.
In general, if n is the number of threes in the pattern, then (n+1) represents the number of ones in the product, and n represents the number of 5 along with one 6.

45.   ANSWER: 2.5

SOLUTION: $a^3 + b^3 = (a + b)(a^2 - 2ab + b^2)$
$a + b = 1$ and $a^2 + b^2 = 2$ implies that $a^2 + 2ab + b^2 = 1$
Subtracting $a^2 + b^2 = 2$ from $a^2 + 2ab + b^2 = 1$ gives $2ab = ‑1$ and $ab = ‑0.5$.
So $a^3 + b^3 = (a + b)[(a^2 + b^2) - ab] = (1)[(2) - (‑0.5)] = (1)(2.5) = 2.5$.

RUBRIC
3 possible points
1 point (content): Realize that $a + b = 1$ & $a^2 + b^2 = 2$
        implies $a^2 + 2ab + b^2 = 1$.
1 point (content): Algebra is done correctly.
1 point (clarity): The explanation is clearly written.

46.   ANSWER: 48

SOLUTION: This is an application of 1+3+5+7+.... Since the total is known, there are two ways to arrive at the number of groups. One is to keep adding the odd numbers until 2250 is reached. The other is to realize that 1+3=4, 1+3+5=9, 1+3+5+7=16, etc. So, each new group raises the total to the next consecutive square counting number (1^2, 2^2, 3^2, 4^2, etc.), so you only need to find the largest square contained in 2250, which is 2209. That square root gives 47 groups, and then you add one more for the 48th group.

RUBRIC
4 possible points
1 point (content): Realize that the pattern is the sum of odd
        counting numbers.
1 point (content): Realize that the total is the group number
        squared.
1 point (content): Arithmetic is done correctly.
1 point (clarity): The explanation is clearly written.

47.   ANSWER: $n^2 - n$

SOLUTION: Any term T can be defined by taking the position of the number in the sequence. Term 1 occupies the first place in the sequence and $1^2 - 1 = 0$. Term 2 occupies the second place and $2^2 - 2 = 2$. Term 3 occupies the third place and $3^2 - 3 = 6$, etc. In general, you have $n^2 - n$ for any term where n is the number of the term in the sequence.

48.   ANSWER: 2^9 and 5^9 or 512 and 1,953,125

SOLUTION: Since $1,000,000,000 = 10^9$, then $10^9 = (2 \times 5)^9$
or $2^9 \times 5^9$.

49.   ANSWER: 0

SOLUTION: The 300 terms can be grouped into 150 odd-even
pairs of numbers each with a sum of 1. Therefore, the sum of
the first 300 terms is (1)(150) = 150. The average of the first 300
terms is $\frac{150}{300}$ = 0.5. The 200 terms can be grouped into 100
odd-even pairs of numbers each with a sum of 1. The sum of
the first 200 terms is (1)(100) = 100. The average of the first 200
terms is $\frac{100}{200}$ = 0.5. Therefore, the difference of the two means
is 0.

RUBRIC
3 possible points*
1 point (content): Realize the value of adding pairs of terms.
1 point (content): The arithmetic is correct.
1 point (clarity): The explanation is well written.

* While it is possible to do this problem by extending the pattern to
300 terms and doing it arithmetically or even using formulas, one
characteristic of a good problem solver is the ability to recognize
helpful patterns. Recognition of the "two consecutive term sum of
1" should be rewarded in this case, perhaps even by awarding a
bonus point.

50.   ANSWER: 499,500 ordered pairs

SOLUTION: Set H has 1,000 elements. If a = 1, then b can be
any of the other 999 elements. If a = 3, then b can be any of
the 998 larger entries and so on. Thus, the number of possible
ordered pairs is 999 + 998 + ... 1 = $\frac{(999)(1000)}{2}$ = 499,500.

51.   ANSWER: 1,000,000

SOLUTION: Try a smaller problem. The sum of the first 10
odd counting numbers is 100, and the sum of the first 10 even
counting numbers is 110. The difference is 10, which is the
number of even and odd counting numbers used in each instance.
This occurs since we begin with the first odd counting number
being 1 and the first even counting number being 2. Therefore,
the even counting numbers will be 1 greater for each case. Since
we are working with the first 1,000,000 even and odd counting
numbers, the difference is 1,000,000.

52.   ANSWER: 294, 448, 648

SOLUTION: The pattern is the difference between a counting
number cubed and that same counting number's square. 0
represents $1^3 - 1^2$, 4 represents $2^3 - 2^2$, 18 is $3^3 - 3^2$, 48 is $4^3 - 4^2$,
100 is $5^3 - 5^2$, 180 is $6^3 - 6^2$, then 294 = $7^3 - 7^2$, 448 = $8^3 - 8^2$, and
648 = $9^3 - 9^2$.

53.   ANSWER: 113

SOLUTION: The @ operation requires you to find the sum of the
squares of each number being operated upon ($3^2 + 4^2 = 9 + 16 = 25$).
Thus, $7^2 + 8^2 = 49 + 64 = 113$.

54.   ANSWER: $x = \frac{^-7}{3}$

SOLUTION: (NOTE this leads to composition of functions.)

$\boxed{x}$ = $x + 3$

$\boxed{\boxed{x}}$ = $x^2 + 6x + 9 - 4 = x^2 + 6x + 5$

$x^2 - \boxed{\boxed{x}}$ = 5

or $x^2 - \boxed{x+3}$ - 4 = 5

Substituting, $x^2 - (x^2 + 6x + 5) - 4 = 5$
$\qquad\qquad x^2 - x^2 - 6x - 5 - 4 = 5$
$\qquad\qquad\qquad\qquad ^-6x - 9 = 5$
$\qquad\qquad\qquad\qquad\qquad ^-6x = 14$

$\qquad\qquad\qquad\qquad x = \frac{^-7}{3}$

RUBRIC
4 possible points
1 point (content): Realize

$\boxed{x+3}$ = $x^2 + 6x + 5$

1 point (content): Realize

$x^2 - \boxed{\boxed{x}}$ = 5 or $x^2 - (x^2 + 6x + 5) - 4 = 5$

1 point (content): The algebra is correct.

1 point (clarity): The explanation is clearly written.

55.   ANSWER: 3, 6, 12

SOLUTION: Let the first term of the geometric progression be $\frac{x}{r}$
and let the common ratio be r. Then

[1] $x\left(\dfrac{1}{r}\right) + 1 + r) = 21$ and

[2] $\left(\dfrac{1}{x}\right)(\left(\dfrac{1}{r}\right) + 1 + r) = \dfrac{7}{12}$

Dividing [1] by [2] gives $x^2 = 36$ and $x = \pm 6$

Substituting in [1] gives $r = 2$. The three terms are $\frac{6}{2}$, 6, and
(6)(2) or 3, 6, 12.

The sum of the terms is 3 + 6 + 12 = 21. The sum of the
reciprocals is $\frac{2}{6} + \frac{1}{6} + \frac{1}{(2)(6)} = \frac{4}{12} + \frac{2}{12} + \frac{1}{12} = \frac{7}{12}$. Note
that using $^-6$ for x gives irrational solutions.

56.   ANSWER: 543,345

SOLUTION: You can only form 2 six-digit numbers under these conditions: 312,132 and 231,213 and 312,132 + 231,213 = 543,345.

Begin with the 3s.

If the three is the first digit, it must also be the fifth digit such as 3 __ __ __ 3 __ .

If the one is the second digit, it must also occupy the fourth place such as 3 1 __ 1 3 __ allowing 2s to complete the number.

If the one is the third digit, it must also occupy the fifth place, which is not possible since a 3 is already there.

If the one is the fourth digit, it must also occupy the sixth place such as 3 __ __ 1 3 1, but that would cause the 2s to be adjacent, which is not allowed.

Therefore, 312,132 is the only possible six-digit number with three being the first digit.

If the three is the second digit, it must also be the sixth digit such as __ 3 __ __ __ 3 .

If one is the first digit, it must also occupy the third place such as 1 3 1 __ __ 3, but that would cause the 2s to be adjacent, which is not allowed.

If the one is the third digit, it must also occupy the fifth place such as __ 3 1 __ 1 3, allowing 2s to complete the number.

The 3s cannot occupy the third or fourth places.

Therefore, 312,132 and 231,213 are the only possible values.

57.   SOLUTION: Consider a 3-digit number, xyz. Rewrite xyz, using expanded notation, as $100x + 10y + z$. Focus on $100x$ in the expanded form of xyz, because once it is seen how to rewrite this, the other places are similar. Using the clue of knowing one term of the final answer needs to be x, rewrite $100x$ to become $99x + x$. The x is now isolated and 99 is a multiple of 3, which is always divisible by 3. Using the same technique for $10y$,

$$xyz = 100x + 10y + z$$
$$= (99 + 1)x + (9 + 1)y + z$$
$$= 99x + x + 9y + y + z$$
$$= 99x + 9y + x + y + z$$

It is known that $99x$ and $9y$ will always be divisible by 3, assuring the ability to factor 3 out of those two terms. The only thing left to consider is $x + y + z$, which is the sum of the digits. If the sum $x + y + z$ is divisible by 3, then the original number can be expressed as a multiple of 3. That is, if $x + y + z = 3n$, where n is a digit, $99x + 9y + (x + y + z)$ becomes $99x + 9y + 3n$, or $3(33x + 3y + n)$. This shows that xyz is a multiple of 3, making it divisible by 3. If the sum of the digits is not a multiple of 3, the original number cannot be expressed as a multiple of 3. The process would be similar for any counting number, no matter the number of digits.

RUBRIC
7 possible points
1 point (content): Realize the need to use expanded notation.

1 point (content): Realize the need to isolate the digits.
1 point (content): Realize that any power of 10 can be expressed as 99...9 + 1.
1 point (content): Realize the need to show xyz as a multiple of 3.
1 point (content): Realize that a multiple of 3 must be divisible by 3.
2 point (clarity): The explanation is clearly written.

58.   SOLUTION: Consider a 3-digit number, xyz, where x, y, and z are digits. Rewrite xyz, using expanded notation, as $100x + 10y + z$. Focus on $100x$ in the expanded form of xyz, because once it is seen how to rewrite this, the other places are similar. Using the clue of knowing one term of the final answer needs to be x, rewrite $100x$ to become $99x + x$. The x is now isolated. The 99 is a multiple of 9 and is always divisible by 9. Using the same technique for $10y$,

$$xyz = 100x + 10y + z$$
$$= (99 + 1)x + (9 + 1)y + z$$
$$= 99x + x + 9y + y + z$$
$$= 99x + 9y + x + y + z$$

It is known that $99x$ and $9y$ will always be divisible by 9, assuring the ability to factor 9 out of those two terms. The only thing left to consider is $x + y + z$, which is the sum of the digits. If the sum $x + y + z$ is divisible by 9, then the original number can be expressed as a multiple of 9. That is, if $x + y + z = 9n$, where n is a digit, $99x + 9y + (x + y + z)$ becomes $99x + 9y + 9n$, or $9(11x + y + n)$. This shows that xyz is a multiple of 9, making it divisible by 9. If the sum of the digits is not a multiple of 9, the original number cannot be expressed as a multiple of 9. The process would be similar for any counting number, no matter the number of digits.

RUBRIC
7 possible points
1 point (content): Realize the need to use expanded notation.
1 point (content): Realize the need to isolate the digits.
1 point (content): Realize that any power of 10 can be expressed as 99...9 + 1.
1 point (content): Realize the need to show xyz as a multiple of 9.
1 point (content): Realize that a multiple of 9 must be divisible by 9.
2 point (clarity): The explanation is clearly written.

59.   SOLUTION: Suppose the number under consideration is 78. We could write it as 70 + 8. That could be rewritten as 7(10) + 8. Ten is always divisible by 2 and so will any multiple of it. 7(10) could be rewritten as 7(5)(2) to emphasize the presence of divisibility by 2. Focusing on the 8, it can be written as 4(2). Given this, 78 could be rewritten as 7(5)(2) + 4(2). Factoring gives 2[7(5) + 4], showing that 78 is a multiple of 2 and therefore divisible by 2.

In general, consider xy, where y represents the ones digit of the number and x represents all the other digits in the number (x might not be a single digit, but it will be some counting number). Then, $xy = 10x + y$, and 10 is always divisible by 2. If y is even, it can be expressed as $2z$. Substituting $2z$ for y, $xy = 10x + 2z$ and factoring gives $2(5x + z)$, meaning that xy is a multiple of 2 and therefore divisible by 2. If y is not even, it cannot be expressed as a multiple of 2 and, therefore, the 2 cannot be factored out of xy. If a 2 cannot be factored out of xy, then xy is not a multiple of 2 and, therefore, xy is not divisible by 2.

RUBRIC
7 possible points
1 point (content): Realize the need to use expanded notation.

1 point (content): Realize that any multiple of 10 is divisible by 2.
1 point (content): Realize the need to express the ones digit as a multiple of 2.
1 point (content): Realize the need to show xy as a multiple of 2.
1 point (content): Realize that a multiple of 2 must be divisible by 2.
2 point (clarity): The explanation is clearly written.

60.   SOLUTION: For example 3,572 could be written as 3,500 + 72. That could be rewritten as (35)(100) + 72. One hundred is always divisible by 4 and so is any multiple of one hundred. (35)(100) could be rewritten as (35)(25)(4) to emphasize the presence of divisibility by 4. Focusing on the 72, it can be written as (18)(4). Given this, 3,572 could be rewritten as (35)(25)(4) + (18)(4). Factoring gives (4)[(35)(25) + 18], showing that 3,572 is a multiple of 4 and therefore divisible by 4.

Using 95,736 as an example, we could write it as 95,000 + 736. That could be rewritten as 95(1,000) + 736. One thousand is always divisible by 8 and so is any multiple of one thousand. (95)(1,000) could be rewritten as (95)(125)(8) to emphasize the presence of divisibility by 8. Focusing on the 736, it can be written as (92)(8). Given this, 95,736 could be rewritten as (95)(1,000) + (92)(8). Factoring gives (8)[(95)(125) + 92], showing that 95736 is a multiple of 8, and therefore, divisible by 8.

In general, consider the number xyz, where yz represents the tens and ones digits of the number and x represents all the other digits in the number (x might not be a single digit, but it will be some counting number). In expanded notation, $xyz = 100x + yz$, and 100 is always divisible by 4. If yz is a multiple of 4, it can be shown as $4q$, where q is some whole number. Then $xyz = 100x + 8q$. Factoring gives $(8)(25x + q)$, meaning that xyz is a multiple of 4 and therefore divisible by 4. If yz is not a multiple of 4, it cannot be expressed as $4q$ and, therefore, the 4 cannot be factored out of yz. If 4 cannot be factored out of yz, then yz is not a multiple of 4 and, therefore, yz is not divisible by 4.

RUBRIC
7 possible points
1 point (content): Realize the need to use expanded notation.
1 point (content): Realize that any multiple of 100 is divisible by 4.
1 point (content): Know to express the number formed by the tens and ones digits as a multiple of 4.
1 point (content): Realize the need to show xyz as a multiple of 4.
1 point (content): Realize that a multiple of 4 must be divisible by 4.
2 point (clarity): The explanation is clearly written.

61.   SOLUTION: Using 95,736 as an example, we could write it as 95,000 + 736. That could be rewritten as 95(1,000) + 736. One thousand is always divisible by 8 and so will any multiple of one thousand. (95)(1,000) could be rewritten as (95)(125)(8) to emphasize the presence of divisibility by 8. Focusing on the 736, it can be written as (92)(8). Given this, 95,736 could be rewritten as (95)(125)(8) + (92)(8). Factoring gives (8)[(95)(125) + 92], showing that 95,736 is a multiple of 8 and, therefore, divisible by 8.

In general, consider the number $wxyz$, where xyz represents the hundreds, tens, and ones digits of the number and w represents all the other digits in the number (w might not be a single digit, but it will be some counting number). In expanded notation, $wxyz = 1,000w + xyz$, and 1,000 is always divisible by 8. If xyz is a

multiple of 8, it can be expressed as $8q$, where q is some whole number. Then $wxyz = 1,000w + 8q$ and factoring gives $(8)(125w + q)$, meaning that $wxyz$ is a multiple of 8 and therefore divisible by 8. If xyz is not a multiple of 8, it cannot be expressed as $8q$ and, therefore, the 8 cannot be factored out of xyz. If 8 cannot be factored out of xyz, then xyz is not a multiple of 8 and, therefore, xyz is not divisible by 8.

RUBRIC
7 possible points
1 point (content): Realize the need to use expanded notation.
1 point (content): Realize that any multiple of 1,000 is divisible by 8.
1 point (content): Know to show the number formed by the hundreds, tens, and ones digits as a multiple of 8.
1 point (content): Realize the need to show $wxyz$ as a multiple of 8.
1 point (content): Realize that a multiple of 8 must be divisible by 8.
2 point (clarity): The explanation is clearly written.

62.   SOLUTION: The letters $a, b, c, d, e, f, g, h, j, k, m, n, o, p, q$ represent digits
Divisibility by 2 involves creating a 2 part number expressed as $10a + b$.

Note that 2 and 10 can be expressed as 2^1 and 10^1.

Divisibility by 4 involves creating a 2 part number expressed as $100c + de$.

Note that 4 and 100 can be expressed as 2^2 and 10^2.

Divisibility by 8 involves creating a 2 part number expressed as $1,000f + ghk$.

Note that 8 and 1,000 can be expressed as 2^3 and 10^3.

There is a pattern that could be extended to 16 expressed as 2^4 and 10,000 as 10^4. Thus, for a number to be divisible by 16 it would be split into a two part number expressed as $10,000m + nopq$. Then, $nopq$ would need to be able to be expressed as a multiple of 16.

RUBRIC
6 possible points
1 point (content): Realize the need to use expanded notation.
1 point (content): Realize that 10^x is divisible by 2^x.
1 point (content): Realize the need to split the number into two parts involving 10^x for the given 2^x.
1 point (content): Generalize correctly.
2 point (clarity): The explanation is clearly written.

63.   ANSWER: 31

SOLUTION: No multiple of 4 will end in 1, 3, or 5. The only one digit number would be 4. Since we can only look for numbers that end in 2 and 4 that are less than 60, the two digit multiples of 4 would be restricted to 12, 24, 32, 44, and 52. The three digit numbers would also have to end in 12, 24, 32, 44, and 52 but could only begin with 1, 2, 3, 4, and 5. Therefore 5 x 5 = 25 is the number of three digit possibilities.

So 25 + 5 + 1 = 31 possibilities exist.

64.   ANSWER: 12

        SOLUTION: This could be solved by guess and check.
                          OR
        To solve it algebraically, let x be the missing number. Then,

$$\frac{2+7+11+15+x}{5} = 9.4$$

$$\frac{35+x}{5} = 9.4$$

$$35 + x = (9.4)(5)$$

$$35 + x = 47$$

$$x = 47 - 35$$

$$x = 12$$

65.   ANSWER: Will vary

        SOLUTION: Let p be the phone number and a be the age.
        Multiplying the phone by two gives $2p$
        Adding five gives $2p + 5$
        Multiplying by 50 gives $50(2p + 5) = 100p + 250$
        Adding the age gives $100p + 250 + a$
        Adding 365 gives $100p + 250 + a + 365 = 100p + a + 615$
        Subtracting 615 gives $100p + a$

        Since p is multiplied by 100, the product will be p with zeros in the
        ones and tens places of the product. However, since zero is the
        additive identity, adding the age will not impact the answer (unless
        the individual is 100 years old or older).

        RUBRIC
        5 possible points
        1 point (content): Realize the need to use p, and a for the values.
        1 point (content): The translation of the problem to algebraic
                            format is correct.
        1 point (content): The algebra and arithmetic is done correctly.
        1 point (content): The values for p, and a are interpreted correctly.
        1 point (clarity): The explanation is clearly written.

66.   SOLUTION: Let the three die be x, y, and z.
        Select x. Multiplying by 2 gives $2x$
        Adding 5 gives $2x + 5$
        Multiplying by 5 gives $5(2x + 5) = 10x + 25$
        Adding a second die gives $10x + 25 + y$
        Multiplying by 10 gives $10(10x + 25 + y) = 100x + 250 + 10y$
        Adding the remaining die gives $100x + 250 + 10y + z$
        Subtracting 250 gives $100x + 10y + z$
        We know x, y, and z are digits.
        $100x + 10y + z$ is expanded notation for a 3 digit number with x in
        the hundreds place, y in the tens place, and z in the ones place.
        But x, y, and z are the values of the original three die.

        RUBRIC
        5 possible points
        1 point (content): Realize the need to use x, y, and z for the die
                            values.
        1 point (content): The translation of the problem to algebraic
                            format is correct.
        1 point (content): The algebra and arithmetic is done correctly.
        1 point (content): The values for x, y, and z are interpreted
                            correctly.
        1 point (clarity): The explanation is clearly written.

67.   ANSWER: 1296

        SOLUTION: On a 1 x 1 checkerboard, there is only 1 rectangle

        On a 2 x 2 checkerboard, there are 9 rectangles (four small 1 x 1
        squares, one large 2 x 2 square and four 1 x 2 rectangles)

        On a 3 x 3 chessboard, there are 36 rectangles (9 small 1 x 1
        squares, one large 3 x 3 square, four 2 x 2 squares, six 1 x 3
        rectangles, twelve 1 x 2 rectangles, four 2 x 3 rectangles)

        Also notice that the values are perfect squares of triangular
        numbers (1, 3, 6, 10, 15, 21, ...)

        1 x 1   1st triangular number 1^2 or 1 rectangle
        2 x 2   2nd triangular number 3^2 or 9 rectangles
        3 x 3   3rd triangular number 6^2 or 36 rectangles
        4 x 4   4th triangular number 10^2 or 100 rectangles
        5 x 5   5th triangular number 15^2 or 225 rectangles
        6 x 6   6th triangular number 21^2 or 441 rectangles
        7 x 7   7th triangular number 28^2 or 784 rectangles
        8 x 8   8th triangular number 36^2 or 1,296 rectangles

68.   ANSWER: $\dfrac{1}{3}$

        SOLUTION: NOTE: $_{10}C_6$ means the number of combinations of
        10 things picked 6 at a time. There are $_{10}C_6$ = 210 different sets
        that could be picked. If the second smallest pick is 3, then one
        number must be picked from {1, 2} and four must be picked from
        {4, 5, 6, 7, 8, 9, 10}. There are $(_2C_1)(_7C_4)$ = (2)(35) = 70 ways to
        do this. So, the probability is $\dfrac{70}{210}$ or $\dfrac{1}{3}$.

        RUBRIC

        4 possible points
        1 point (content): Realize 1 number must come from {1, 2}
        1 point (content): Realize 1 number must come from {4, 5, 6, 7, 8,
                            9, 10}.
        1 point (content): All arithmetic is done correctly.
        1 point (clarity): The explanation is clearly written.

69.   ANSWER: $\dfrac{2}{3}$

        SOLUTION: Call the two marbles Kw (Known white) and Uw or
        Ub (for either Unknown black or Unknown white). There are four
        possible outcomes after our first drawing:
                Kw is drawn, leaving Uw in the bag
                Kw is drawn, leaving Ub in the bag
                Uw is drawn, leaving Kw in the bag
                Ub is drawn, leaving Kw in the bag
        Since a white marble is drawn, the fourth event did not occur. So,
        there are three possible outcomes, two of which have a white
        marble left, so the probability is $\dfrac{2}{3}$.

        RUBRIC

        3 possible points
        1 point (content): Express the 4 possible events.
        1 point (content): Realize that 1 event cannot happen.
        1 point (clarity): The explanation is clearly written.

70.   ANSWER: 1 or 100%

SOLUTION: The sum of the digits on the balls 1 + 4 + 7 + 7 + 8 = 27. Therefore, any number created by these five digits must be a multiple of 3 and 9. Therefore, none of the five-digit numbers can be prime, revealing that all are composite.

71.   ANSWER: 4

SOLUTION: 0! + 1! + 2! + 3! + 4! is all you have to worry about. Anything above 5! must end in at least one zero. So, you have the sum of 0!=1 , 1!=1, 2!=2, 3!=6, and 4!=24, or 1 + 1 + 2 + 6 + 24 = 34. The ones digit of 4 is now added to zero, giving a final sum that has a ones digit of 4.

RUBRIC

4 possible points
1 point (content): Knowledge of factorial.
1 point (content): Realization that 0! = 1.
1 point (content): Realization that all factorials > 4! end in at least one zero.
1 point (clarity): The explanation is clearly written.

72.   SOLUTION: Dividing both sides by $b - a$ is dividing by zero, which cannot be done.

RUBRIC
3 possible points
1 point (content): Realize $b - a$ represents zero.
1 point (content): Realize division by zero is undefined.
1 point (clarity): The explanation is clearly written.

73.   SOLUTION: $121_{10} = (1 \times 10^2) + (2 \times 10^1) + (1 \times 10^0) = 100 + 20 + 1$.

The base b could be used so the inside of each parentheses could be expressed as $(1 \times b^2) + (2 \times b^1) + (1 \times b^0)$, which is also $b^2 + 2b + 1$, or $(b + 1)^2$.

But, $(b + 1)^2$ is a perfect square in any number base b since $(b + 1) \times (b + 1) = (b + 1)^2$.

For example,
$121_5 = (1 \times 5^2) + (2 \times 5^1) + (1 \times 5^0)$
$= 25 + 10 + 1$
$= 36$

$(b + 1) \times (b + 1)$ would be

$(5 + 1) \times (5 + 1) = 6 \times 6$ or 36_{10}, which is 121_5.

74.   ANSWER: 2

SOLUTION: Let x be one number and y be the other.

Then $x + y = 50$ and $xy = 25$. Then $\dfrac{1}{x} + \dfrac{1}{y}$ is what you are

looking for. $\dfrac{1}{x} + \dfrac{1}{y} = \dfrac{y}{xy} + \dfrac{x}{xy} = \dfrac{x + y}{xy}$.

Since $x + y = 50$ and $xy = 25$, then $\dfrac{x + y}{xy} = \dfrac{50}{25} = 2$.

Remember, this problem does not ask for x or y, but only the sum of the reciprocals of the numbers.
          OR
Let x be one number and y be the other. Then $x + y = 50$

and $xy = 25$. Then $\dfrac{1}{x} + \dfrac{1}{y}$ is what you are looking for.

$\dfrac{1}{x} + \dfrac{1}{y} = \dfrac{y}{xy} + \dfrac{x}{xy} = \dfrac{x + y}{xy}$.

Since $xy = 25$, $x = \dfrac{25}{y}$ and $y = \dfrac{25}{x}$. Substituting these in x

$+ y = 50$ gives $\dfrac{25}{y} + \dfrac{25}{x} = 50$. Multiplying both sides of this

equation by $\dfrac{1}{25}$ gives $\left(\dfrac{1}{25}\right)\left(\dfrac{25}{y} + \dfrac{25}{x}\right) = \left(\dfrac{1}{25}\right)(50)$, or

$\dfrac{1}{y} + \dfrac{1}{x} = 2$, which is the answer.

75.   ANSWER: Time will vary.
Shortcut involves letting $a - 1 = 1234567890$.

SOLUTION: Letting $a - 1 = 1234567890$, the problem becomes

$\dfrac{a - 1}{a^2 - (a - 1)(a + 1)} = \dfrac{a - 1}{a^2 - a^2 - 1} = a - 1$.

RUBRIC
4 possible points
1 point (content): Realize the need to let $a - 1 = 1234567890$.
1 point (content): Realize $a = 1234567891$ and $a + 1 = 1234567892$.
1 point (content): The algebra and arithmetic is done correctly.
1 point (clarity): The explanation is clearly written.

76.   ANSWER: 88

SOLUTION: The multiples of 11 = {11, 22, 33, 44, ... 110. 121, 132, ...}.
The pair of digits reduces the set to {11, 22, 33, 44, 55, 66, 77, 88, 99}.

Even cuts the set to {22, 44, 66, 88}.

Multiply the digits and see which product is both a square and a cube.
8x8 = 64, which is 8^2 and 4^3.

77.   SOLUTION: The value of each letter is listed below it.
A B C D E F G H I J K L M N O P Q R S T U V W X Y Z
1 2 3 4 5 6 7 8 9 10 11 12 13 14 15 16 17 18 19 20 21 22 23 24 25 26

Find the sum of the value of the letters and put a % after it.
H A R D W O R K
8 1 18 4 23 15 18 11 = 98%

K N O W L E D G E
11 14 15 23 12 5 4 7 5 = 96%

But,

A T T I T U D E
1 20 20 9 20 21 4 5 = 100 %

78.   ANSWER: 194

SOLUTION: The sum of the entries in the first row is M + 21 + 94, or M + 115. The bottom entry in the first column must be 112 since it + M + 3 = 115.

The known diagonal is 112 + Center + 94 and also M + 115. From that, Center = M – 91.

The second row is 3 + M – 91 + Right = M + 115. From that, Right = 203.

The third column must equal M + 115 = 94 + 203 + BottomR. From that, BottomR = M – 182.

The Upper Left to Lower Right diagonal is M + M – 91 + M – 182 = M + 115.

Solving for M yields M = 194.

M	21	94
3	103	203
112	185	12

RUBRIC
7 possible points
1 point (content): Recognize the need to start with top row.
1 point (content): Recognize the need to solve left column.
1 point (content): Recognize the need to solve for center element.
1 point (content): Recognize the need to solve right column.
1 point (content): Recognize the need to solve Upper Left – Lower Right diagonal.
1 point (content): Computations are correct.
1 point (clarity): The explanation is clearly written.

79.   ANSWER: 15

SOLUTION: Let x be the given number. The kid's calculation would be:

$\frac{x - 9}{3} = 43$, which leads to $x - 9 = 129$, and $x = 138$.

So, the given number is 138, and doing the computation correctly,

$$\frac{138 - 3}{9} = \frac{135}{9} = 15.$$

80.   ANSWER: 7,200,000,000 different numbers

SOLUTION: Since the first digit cannot be a 0 or 1, the first choice can only have 8 different digits. Since the fourth digit cannot be a 0, the fourth digit can only have 9 different choices. The remaining digits can all have a possible 10 different digits. Thus, 8 x 10 x 10 x 9 x 10 x 10 x 10 x 10 x 10 x 10 = 7,200,000,000. Note that we do not eliminate specialty numbers like 911 and 411 from area code elimination here, when, in reality, they would not be used as area codes.

81.   ANSWER: $\frac{10}{1,000}$ or $\frac{1}{100}$ or 0.01

SOLUTION: Since $1,000^2 = 1,000,000$, there are 1,000 perfect squares between 1 and 1,000,000 inclusive because 1 is 1^2 and 1,000,000 is $1,000^2$. For a number to be a perfect square and cube it must be a perfect 6th power. Only 10 of these are possible, $1^6, 2^6, 3^6, 4^6, ..., 10^6$ (since $10^6 = 1,000,000$). Therefore, the probability is $\frac{10}{1,000}$.

82.   ANSWER: 7

SOLUTION: x = number of days spent eating
          $(20 - x)$ = number of days not eating
So, $2x - 3(20 - x) = 5$
    $2x - 60 + 3x = 5$
          $5x = 65$
          $x = 13$
    $20 - 13 = 7$

He did not eat for 7 days.

83.   ANSWER: $8 = 3! + \frac{3!}{3}$ and $9 = 3! + 3! - 3$

SOLUTION: $3! = 6$

$3! + \frac{3!}{3} = 6 + \frac{6}{3} = 6 + 2 = 8.$
$9 = 3! + 3! - 3 = 6 + 6 - 3 = 9.$
There may be other possible solutions as well.

84.   ANSWER: There is only one, 21,978.

SOLUTION: Suppose $abcde$ x 4 = $edcba$ where a, b, c, d, and e are digits.
          $4a$ must be less than 10
          a must be even since e x 4 will be even
          a must be 2
          e must be 8
          Since a = 2, ab must be < 25 since 25 x 4 = 100
          Since e = 8, B cannot be 3 since 23 x 4 > 89
          b cannot be 2 because ba must be a multiple of 4 and 22 is not
          Therefore, b = 1.
          So far, $abcde$ = $21cd8$ x 4 = $8dc12$.
          Since d8 x 4 must end in 12, checking shows that only 28 or 78 end in 12.
          28 would cause c to be 1, which will not work if you check.
          If d is 7, then a value of 9 for c will give a reversible product.

85.   ANSWER: 25 Goldanian Dollars

SOLUTION: If x is a person's weekly salary, then a person's take-home salary is represented by $x - (x)\left(\frac{x}{100}\right)$ which simplifies to $-\left(\frac{x^2}{100}\right) + x$. Graphing

$$y = - \left(\frac{x^2}{100} \right) + x$$ produces a parabola with a maximum value

for y of 25 dollars when a person makes $(50)(x)$.

86.   ANSWER: 315 two-scoop cones

SOLUTION: With 14 different ice cream flavors, you can make 105 two-scoop combinations. The key is that you can have a vanilla-vanilla scoop. By trying a smaller problem, you can see a pattern. If you only had 4 flavors: *a, b, c,* and *d,* you could have *aa, ab, ac, ad, bb, bc, bd, cc, cd, dd.* With 4 flavors, you have 4 with *a,* then you have 3 with *b* since *ba* is already covered, then 2 with *c* and 1 with *d* or 4 + 3 + 2 + 1 = 10. For 14 flavors 14 + 13 + 12 + 11 + 10 + 9 + 8 + 7 + 6 + 5 + 4 + 3 + 2 + 1 = 105. Since you have only three cones, you can have 105 combinations with each cone or 105 x 3 possible 2-scoop cones.

87.   ANSWER: 64

SOLUTION: Let *a* and *b* represent the two unequal whole numbers. Then $64(a - b) = a^2 - b^2$. Factoring yields $64(a - b) = (a - b)(a + b)$. Since *a* and *b* are not equal, $(a - b)$ does not equal zero. Therefore, you can divide both sides by $(a - b)$ which yields $64 = a + b$. To solve the problem, you do not have to know the values of *a* and *b,* just the sum of *a* and *b* which is 64, the total number of books!

88.   ANSWER: 278

SOLUTION: Consider three cases: AB85, A85B, and 85AB.

For AB85:
Nine choices exist for A (1, 2, 3, 4, 5, 6, 7, 8, 9) and ten for B (0, 1, 2, 3, 4, 5, 6, 7, 8, 9) which gives 90 numbers, but 85 would be one of those numbers and 8585 cannot be a possibility since the problem states the digit pattern 85 once and only once. Therefore AB85 would have 89 possible 4-digit numbers. For A85B, nine choices exist again for A and ten for B yield 90 numbers. For 85AB, ten choices exist for A and ten for B but again 8,585 cannot be counted, thus 99 numbers exist. Therefore 89 + 90 + 99 = 278.

89.   ANSWER: 210

SOLUTION: Since the mean value of the 20 unique numbers is 20, the sum of all the numbers must be 400. Because you want to find the greatest possible value that allows these conditions to be met, you need to use the smallest possible 19 numbers to add to the largest. In other words,

$$\frac{1+2+3+4+5+6+7+8+9+10+11+12+13+14+15+16+17+18+19+X}{20} = 20$$

$$190 + X = 400$$
$$X = 210$$

90.   ANSWER: ⁻4

SOLUTION: Since there are five numbers in the set and the mean is 12, the sum of the set must equal 60. If the smallest value is removed, there will only be four numbers in the new set and the

mean of this set is 16, then the sum of the four numbers must be 64.

Let *n* be the smallest number and *r* be the sum of the other 4.

Then $n + r = 60$ and also $r = 64$.

Substituting $r = 64$ in the first equation yields $n + 64 = 60$.

Therefore, $n = ⁻4$.

RUBRIC
4 possible points
1 point (content): Realize the sum of the 5 numbers must be 60.
1 point (content): Realize the sum of the 4 numbers must be 64.
1 point (content): Realize that the smallest value + 64 = 60.
1 point (clarity): The explanation is clearly written.

91.   ANSWER: Zero

SOLUTION: For $\frac{a^2}{4}$ to give a remainder of 1, *a* would have to be odd since any even number squared would produce an even number. An even number divided by four will only produce a remainder of 0 or 2. Therefore, *a* is odd. If *a* is odd, then $a + 5$ is even.

Now, let $2n$ represent an even number, then $(2n)^2 = 4n^2$ which shows that any even number squared must be divisible by 4, leaving a remainder of zero.

92.   ANSWER: 67,800,320 ways

SOLUTION: The first senator may be chosen in 100 ways, the second 98 ways (since you cannot chose the second one from the same state as the first one selected), the third 96 ways, the fourth 94 ways, the fifth 92 ways. Once five senators have been selected, divide by 5! (or 120) because the order of the senators is not important. So,

100 x 98 x 96 x 94 x 92 = 8,136,038,400

$$\frac{8136038400}{120} = 67,800,320.$$

93.   ANSWER: yes, 4

SOLUTION: You can represent a two digit number by $10t + u$. If a two digit number is seven times the sum of its digits, then $10t + u = 7(t + u)$ or $10t + u = 7t + 7u$ or $3t = 6u$ or $t = 2u$, which means that the tens digits is twice the units digit. For this to occur, the tens digit must be 2, 4, 6, or 8. That means that the only possible two digit numbers that satisfy this condition are 21, 42, 63, and 84. The sum of the digits of these four possibilities shows that 21 is 7 times 2+1 or 3, 42 is 7 times 4+2 or 6, 63 is 7 times 6 + 3 or 9, and 84 is 7 times 8+4 or 12. Reversing the digits and examining the sum of the digits shows:
        That for 12 you have 1 + 2 = 3 and 12 is 4 times greater.
        That for 24 you have 2 + 4 = 6 and 24 is 4 times greater.
        That for 36 you have 3 + 6 = 9 and 36 is 4 times greater.
        That for 48 you have 4 + 8 = 12 and 48 is 4 times greater.

This shows that *w* is 4 times greater for all cases.

94.   ANSWER: YEAUCF = 307,692 and UCFYEA = 692,307

SOLUTION: Let x = YEA and y = UCF
$9(\text{YEAUCF}) = 9(1000x + y)$
$4(\text{UCFYEA}) = 4(1000y + x)$
Solving, $8996x = 3991y$.
Dividing by 13 gives $692x = 307y$.
692 and 307 are relatively prime, so $x = 307$ and $y = 692$.

YEAUCF = 307,692 and UCFYEA = 692,307

95.   ANSWER: $5.11

SOLUTION: $x679y$ has to be divisible by 72, meaning it must be divisible by both 8 and 9. For divisibility by 8, the last 3 digits must be divisible by 8, or $79y$ has to be divisible by 8. 792 is the only candidate and thus $y = 2$. Now $x6792$ has to be divisible by 9, so $x+6+7+9+2$ has to be divisible by 9 and $x = 3$. So the total bill has to be $ 367.92.

RUBRIC
3 possible points
1 point (content): Realize that $x679y$ has to be divisible by 72.
1 point (content): Apply divisibility rules correctly.
1 point (clarity): The explanation is clearly written.

96.   ANSWER: WHICH = 9; WHAT = 315

SOLUTION: Let WHICH = w
Since WHICH to WHAT is 35 to 1, WHAT = $35w$
WHICH + WHAT = $w + 35w = 36w$

$$\frac{36w}{4} = 9w$$

But this is also WHICH squared, so $9w = w^2$.
Dividing by w gives $9 = w$.
WHAT = $(35)(9) = 315$.

RUBRIC
4 possible points
1 point (content): Realize that WHICH to WHAT is 35 to 1 and means
        WHAT = $35w$.
1 point (content): Realize $9w = w^2$.
1 point (content): The algebra is correct.
1 point (clarity): The explanation is clearly written.

97.   ANSWER: 4,950

SOLUTION:

$$ab + \frac{cd}{100} = \frac{ab + cd}{2} \qquad \text{Writing the decimal part as a fraction over 100}$$

$$2ab + \frac{cd}{50} = ab + cd \qquad \text{Multiplying both sides by 2}$$

$$ab + \frac{cd}{50} = cd \qquad \text{Subtracting } ab \text{ from both sides}$$

Since ab and cd are both integers, $\frac{cd}{50}$ must also be an integer, and cd also has to be less than 100 if it is the decimal part of $ab.cd$. This means $cd = 50$ in order to make $\frac{cd}{50}$ be an integer.

So, $ab + \dfrac{50}{50} = 50$

$$ab + 1 = 50$$
$$ab = 49, \text{ and, } abcd = 4{,}950.$$

OR

The average of the two numbers must end in either a 0.50 or a 0.00, so the last number must be 50 or 00. If it were 0, the average of the number would be itself, in which case the first digits would have to be 0 also. But since the digits are unique, the last number must be 50. So the first number is odd, and differing from it by 1, since the first 2 digits must be one of the numbers (the average is 0.5 away from both numbers). So our desired number is 4,950.

98.   ANSWER: 12 people

SOLUTION: Let x = the number of people and y = the cost per person.

$$288 = xy \text{ or } \frac{288}{x} = y$$

After the two people left,
$$xy = (x - 2)(y + 4.80)$$
$$xy = xy + 4.8x - 2y - 9.6$$
$$2y = 4.8x - 9.6$$

$$(2)\left(\frac{288}{x}\right) = 4.8x - 9.6$$

$$\frac{576}{x} = 4.8x - 9.6$$

$$\frac{5760}{x} = 48x - 96$$

$$120 = x^2 - 2x$$
$$0 = x^2 - 2x - 120$$
$$x^2 - 2x - 120 = 0$$
$$(x + 10)(x - 12) = 0$$
$$x = {}^-10, 12 \text{ but } {}^-10 \text{ does not make sense here.}$$

99.   ANSWER: 29,038 and 85,216

SOLUTION: A Yipper is a five-digit number with alternating even and odd digits, the first being even. The sum of the digits of a Yipper equals 22.

29,038, follows all Yipper rules.
46,714 sums to 22, but the digits are not alternating even and odd.
25,674 has five alternating even and odd digits, but the sum is not 22.
85,216, follows all Yipper rules.
67,452 sums to 24.

100.   ANSWER: $\dfrac{8}{8\%}$

SOLUTION: $\dfrac{8}{8\%} = \dfrac{8}{0.08} = 100.$

101.   ANSWER: Will vary, but you should get the number you started with.

SOLUTION: Let x be the number.
Triple the number gives $3x$
Adding 12 gives $3x + 12$

Dividing by three gives $\dfrac{3x + 12}{3} = x + 4$
Subtracting four gives x

RUBRIC
3 possible points
1 point (content): The algebraic setup is correct.
1 point (content): The arithmetic is correct.
1 point (clarity): The explanation is clearly written.

102.   ANSWER: $9^{9^{9}}$

SOLUTION: There are four candidates for the answer: 999, 99^9, 9^{99}, and 9^{9^9}. Give these, 999 falls from consideration quickly. Using the idea that 99 is close to 100 and 9 is close to 10, 99^9 is going to be close to 100^{10} which is 10^{20}. Similarly, 9^{99} is close to 100^{10} which is certainly larger than 10^{20}. So far 9^{99} is the biggest number written with 3 digits. Many calculators will do 9^9^9 (NOTE - - the symbol "^" is intentionally used in this explanation to convey what would be done on many calculators) as (9^9)^9 because of the logic programmed into them. They see an exponent and use the order of operations saying exponents are done first. The problem is, they read left to right and solve 9^9 first which is 387420489 and then they calculate (387420489)^9, getting 1.966270505 x 10^{77} which is certainly a large number, but nothing like the size of 9^{9^9}. 9^{9^9} has over 350,000,000 digits. If typed using 10 digits per inch, the answer would be over 550 miles long. The order of operations (Parentheses, Exponents, Multiply, Divide, Add, Subtract (PEMDAS)) is fairly well known. However, the next one up in the hierarchy deals with a power to a power and is not so well known, dictating that you start at the top and work down. You can check your calculator's logic with 2^{3^4}. If you enter 2^3^4 without parentheses and get 4096, you know your calculator is finding $2^3 = 8$ first and then computing 8^4 to get 4096. If on the other hand, if you enter 2^(3^4), your calculator computes 3^4 first, giving 2^{81}, which is 2,417,851,639,229,258,349,412,352. Knowing those two values allows you to check the logic your calculator uses. Alas, many calculators provide an incorrect response for 2^{3^4}.

103.   ANSWER: 15 and 24

SOLUTION: If the number is 10t + u, then 3tu = 10t + u or u(3t − 1) = 10t. Therefore either u or 3t − 1 is a multiple of 5, and since u and t are digits, one of them must equal 5. If 3t − 1 = 5, then t = 2 and u = 4, yielding 24. If u = 5, then t = 1, yielding 15.

104.   ANSWER: $0.40

SOLUTION: Let c be the cost of the less expensive item.
c + $6.00 is the cost of the other item
$c + c + \$6.00 = \$6.80$
$2c = \$0.80$
$c = \$0.40$

RUBRIC
3 possible points
1 point (content): Realize the cost of the more expensive item is
        c + $6.00.
1 point (content): The algebra and arithmetic is done correctly.
1 point (clarity): The explanation is clearly written.

105.   ANSWER: 678

SOLUTION: 9 single-digit pages and 90 double-digit pages use 189 digits. 1,926 – 189 = 1,737 digits left for the 3 digit pages.

$\dfrac{1737}{3}$ = 579 three digit pages. Total number of pages is 9 + 90 + 579 = 678 pages.

                OR

189 + 3(x – 99) = 1926
                3x = 2034
                x = 678

RUBRIC
3 possible points
1 point (content): Realize there are 90 2-digit pages, not 89.
1 point (content): Arithmetic and logic are correct.
1 point (clarity): The explanation is clearly written.

106.   SOLUTION: Let abc be the initial 3-digit number, where a, b, and c are digits.

Repeating the initial 3-digit number gives the 6-digit number $abcabc$.

(7)(11)(13) = 1001
(1001)(abc) = $abcabc$

$\dfrac{abcabc}{1001} = \dfrac{(abc)(1001)}{1001} = abc$

RUBRIC
3 possible points
1 point (content): Realize (7)(11)(13) = 1001.
1 point (content): Express $abcabc$ as (1001)(abc).
1 point (clarity): The explanation is clearly written.

107.   ANSWER: 0

SOLUTION: If you write out each binomial you find that the third to last one is (x - x), which would be zero, causing the entire product to be zero.

108.   ANSWER: 12

         SOLUTION: Factoring 48 yields:
                  1, 48
                  2, 24
                  3, 16
                  4, 12
                  6, 8.

         Of these, 6 and 8 produce the least possible sum of 14, but the
         problem does not say that you must only use 2 factors.
         Replacing 6 with 2 and 3 gives 2, 3, 8, and a sum of 13.

         Replacing the 8 with 2 and 4 gives 2, 4, 6, and a sum of 12.

         Replacing the 6 with 2 and 3, and the 8 with 2 and 4 would give 2,
         4, 2, 3, with a sum of 11, but the problem states distinct factors, so
         two 2s are not allowed.

109.   SOLUTION: All whole numbers may be placed in one of three
         categories: $3k$, $3k+1$, or $3k+2$ where k is any whole number.
         Since the pennies were in a square array, square the three
         categories to determine the number of pennies, getting $9k^2$,
         $9k^2+6k+1$, and $9k^2+12k+4$, respectively. The first square array
         would leave no remainder when dividing by 3. The other two
         squares would leave a remainder of 1 when dividing by 3. Thus,
         it is impossible to have a remainder of 2 when dividing a square
         number by 3, so the butler had to be telling a lie.

                            OR

         Using modular arithmetic in base 3,
         0^2 is congruent to 0(mod 3),
         1^2 is congruent to 1(mod 3), and
         2^2 is congruent to 1(mod 3) (i.e. there exists a number $3n$ or $3n+1$
         where n is a positive integer such that it equals a^2 where a is any
         positive integer). The coins are in a square array, and from the
         above we have proven that there can never be two coins left over
         when divided by three.

110.   ANSWER: Take the doubling pay.

         SOLUTION: The daily amounts are computed using 2^{n-1} for
         the amount on the last day and 2^n for the total amount for the
         month. Doubling the amount in a 31-day month gives a total of
         $21,474,936.48, and $10,737,418.24 on the 31st day compared
         with a total of $310,000.00 total taking $10,000 a day. A 30-day
         total is $10,737,418.24 with $5,368,709.12 on the 30th day. A leap
         year total is $5,368,709.12 with $2,684,354.56 on the 29th day. A
         28-day total is $2,684,354.56 with $1,342,177.28 on the 28th day.

         RUBRIC
         4 possible points
         1 point (content): The algebraic setup is correct.
         1 point (content): The arithmetic is correct.
         1 point (content): All possibilities are given.
         1 point (clarity): The explanation is clearly written.

111.   ANSWER: Using Base 5, 44_5 = 24 in base 10.

         SOLUTION: 13 + 31 = 44.
         44 in base 5 = $4 \times 5^1 + 4 \times 5^0$ = 20 + 4 = 24.

112.   ANSWER: 10,880

         SOLUTION: The four numbers are 1,171, 1,999, 3,793, and 3,917.
         a = 1, b = 3, c = 7, and d = 9.
         Since each letter is a final digit in each number, a, b, c, and d
         must be 1, 3, 7, or 9. No prime number greater than 5 ends in
         an even number or a 5. a and c must be 1 or 7 otherwise the
         numbers $addd$ and $aaca$ would be divisible by 3 because the
         respective digit is repeated three times. Thus b and d must be 3
         or 9. Therefore, $bcdb$ can be written in 4 ways:
             b = 3, d = 9, a = 7, c = 1 or 3,193 which is divisible by 31.
             b = 3, d = 9, a = 1, c = 7 or 3,793 which is prime.
             b = 9, d = 3, a = 7, c = 1 or 9,139 which is divisible by 13.
             b = 9, d = 3, a = 1, c = 7 or 9,739 which is prime.

         In both cases where a prime results, c = 7 and a = 1. So, $bdac$
         must be either 9,317 or 3,917. But, 9,317 is divisible by 7 and
         3,917 is prime.

         Therefore a = 1, b = 3, c = 7 and d = 9.

113.   ANSWER: 4

         SOLUTION: A prime greater than three is of the form
         $6n \pm 1$ where n is a counting number.

         $$(6n \pm 1)^2 = 36n^2 \pm 12n + 1$$

         Adding 15 gives $36n^2 \pm 12n + 16$

         Dividing by 12 gives $\dfrac{36n^2 \pm 12n + 16}{12}$ or

         $$\dfrac{12\left(3n^2 \pm 1n + 1\right) + 4}{12}$$

         Doing this division gives a remainder of 4.

         RUBRIC
         4 possible points
         1 point (content): Realize primes greater than three are of the
                            form $6n \pm 1$.
         1 point (content): The algebra is correct.
         1 point (content): Realize $\dfrac{12\left(3n^2 \pm 1n + 1\right) + 4}{12}$ gives a
                            remainder of 4.
         1 point (clarity): The explanation is clearly written.

114.   ANSWER: 6 or 8

         SOLUTION: Multiply both sides by $t \cdot h \cdot r \cdot e \cdot e$

                   yields $\dfrac{f \cdot i \cdot f \cdot t \cdot e \cdot e \cdot n}{f \cdot i \cdot f \cdot t \cdot y} = o \cdot n \cdot e$

         $f \cdot i \cdot f \cdot t$ divides out on the left side leaving $\dfrac{e \cdot e \cdot n}{y} = o \cdot n \cdot e$

         Divide both sides by $e \cdot n$ leaving $\dfrac{e}{y} = o$ so $e = y \cdot o$. Since
         each letter must be different, e could be 6 giving 6 = 2 x 3 or
         e could be 8 since 8 = 2 x 4. e could not be 4, for example,
         because 4 = 2 x 2, and you would not have three different digits.

115. ANSWER: If $n \leq 0$, $2 - n$ is greatest.

If $n = 1$, $\dfrac{2}{n}$ and $2n$ are greatest.

If $n \geq 2$, $2n$ is greatest.

SOLUTION: Making a table helps to show the pattern:

n	$\dfrac{n}{2}$	$\dfrac{2}{n}$	$2n$	$n-2$	$2-n$	
-100	-50	-0.02	-200	-102	102	
-50	-25	-0.04	-100	-52	52	
-10	-5	-0.2	-20	-12	8	
-4	-2	-0.5	-8	-6	6	
-2	-1	-1	-4	-4	4	
-1	-0.5	-2	-2	-3	3	
0	0	-0	-0	-2	2	$n \leq 0$, $2 - n$ is greatest
1	0.5	2	2	-1	1	$n = 1$, $\dfrac{2}{n}$ and $2n$ are greatest
2	1	1	4	0	0	$n \geq 2$, $2n$ is greatest
4	2	0.5	8	2	-2	
10	5	0.2	20	8	-8	
50	25	0.04	100	48	-48	
100	50	0.02	200	48	-48	

116. ANSWER: $12 \times 63 = 21 \times 36$ (and others). Consider a, b, c, and d to be the digits so that $(ab)(cd) = (ba)(dc)$. It will work as long as $ac = bd$.

SOLUTION:

$$(a\,b)(c\,d) = (b\,a)(d\,c)$$
$$(10a + b)(10c + d) = (10b + a)(10d + c)$$
$$100ac + \cancel{10ad} + \cancel{10bc} + bd = 100bd + \cancel{10bc} + \cancel{10ad} + ac$$
$$100ac - ac = 100bd - bd$$
$$99ac = 99bd$$
$$ac = bd$$

117. SOLUTION: If the first number selected is n, then its square is n^2. The next number would be $(n + 1)$, and squaring it would give $n^2 + 2n + 1$. This shows the square of the second number to be $2n + 1$ larger than the first square. So, after finding the first square, add $2n + 1$ to it to get the square of the next larger counting number. Since n could represent any real number, this process is not limited to counting numbers.

RUBRIC
5 possible points
1 point (content): Realize the need to get n^2.
1 point (content): Realize that $(n + 1)^2$ is $n^2 + 2n + 1$.
1 point (content): Realize that $(n + 1)^2 - n^2$ is $2n + 1$.
1 point (content): Realize that the variable use means any real number will work.
1 point (clarity): The explanation is clearly written.

118. ANSWER: You get the number you picked. You are not limited to counting numbers.

SOLUTION: Let x be the chosen number.
Subtracting the original number squared from one greater than that original number squared gives
$$(x + 1)^2 - x^2 = x^2 + 2x + 1 - x^2$$
$$= 2x + 1.$$

Subtracting one gives $2x$.
Dividing by 2 gives x. Since x represents any real number, the process is not limited to counting numbers.

RUBRIC
4 possible points
1 point (content): Realize the need to use a variable.
1 point (content): The algebra and arithmetic is done correctly.
1 point (content): Realizing that the variable represents any real number.
1 point (clarity): Each explanation is clearly written.

119. ANSWER: $\dfrac{1}{5}$, $\dfrac{1}{7}$, $\dfrac{1}{2N - 1}$

SOLUTION: If you add 5 to the numerator and denominator of

$\dfrac{1}{5}$ you get $\dfrac{1+5}{5+5}$ or $\dfrac{6}{10} = \dfrac{3}{5}$, which is $(3)\left(\dfrac{1}{5}\right)$.

If you add 7 to the numerator and denominator of $\dfrac{1}{7}$ you get

$\dfrac{1+7}{7+7}$ or $\dfrac{8}{14} = \dfrac{4}{7}$, which is $(4)\left(\dfrac{1}{7}\right)$.

In general, $\dfrac{1}{2n - 1}$ will be a fraction that will produce a new fraction n times greater when you add the denominator to the numerator and denominator.

$$\frac{1 + 2n - 1}{(2n - 1) + (2n - 1)} = \frac{2n}{4n - 2}$$
$$= \frac{n}{2n - 1}$$
$$= (n)\left(\frac{1}{2n - 1}\right)$$

120. ANSWER: Will vary. One answer is $(x - 8)(x - 23)(x - 1957) \neq 0$.